CW00357713

The Undateable Gay

Dating has never been so hard...

Mark David Woollard

First Published in 2022 by SpellBound Books.
Copyright © Mark David Woollard.

The moral right of the author to be identified as the owner of this Work has been asserted by them in accordance with the Copyright, Designs and Patents Act, 1988.

All rights reserved. No part of this publication may be reproduced, stored in a retrieval system, or transmitted, in any form or by any means, electronic, mechanical, photocopying, recording or otherwise, without the prior permission of the publisher.
This is a work of fiction. All names, characters, places, locations and events in this publication, other than those clearly in the public domain, are fictitious, and any resemblance to actual persons, living or dead, or any actual places, business establishments, locations or events is purely coincidental.

PRINT ISBN:978-1-7396282-3-9

Cover Art © a r t E A S T c r e a t i v e 2021

FOR

Nanny White
Nanny Woollard
Betty
Nancy
Uncle Jim
Aunty Joan
Mummy Inch

Who aren't here to hold a copy but would have been so proud

Chapter One

Hello. My name is Mark Morgan. No relation to Piers. Thank God! Although I was nearly christened Brian. Thank the Lord my parents saw sense and changed their minds at the last minute. I say changed their minds, my mum got my dad by the throat and threatened if he persisted in calling me Brian, she would disown him. He says he wishes he'd disobeyed her orders as he might have had a quieter life had she followed through on her threats.

Can you imagine if I had been called Brian? I was bullied enough at school just for being gay. I dread to think how bad it might have been if I'd been a camp schoolboy called Brian. I mean, not that I've got anything against anyone with that name.

I've just turned forty. They say life begins here. I'm yet to find out. I'm only one day into my fifth decade. But I tell you something, I really thought I might have met my so-called Mr Right by now. But he seems to be AWOL. And it's not through lack of trying, I'll tell you that for nothing.

My profile on a dating site currently reads:

JUST TURNED THIRTY. (Yes, that's a lie but I still get asked for ID, so in for a penny)

NEW ZEALAND SAVVY B LOVER (No, that's not code for alcoholic, I just love a glass)

THEATRE ADDICT (Yes, I am cultured)

AVID SWIMMER (Yes, I admit seeing the scantily clad men in the pool is a bonus, but I genuinely love swimming)

LOVE WALKS IN THE COUNTRY (No, I'm not into dogging)

PARTAKER OF BOTOX (My mother always taught me to look your best)

POSITION: VERSATILE (That's a new addition for me. I've always been a TOP but of late, I've become partial to a bit of bottoming)

Well, I use the term, 'dating site' loosely. It's actually Grindr. Perhaps that's where I'm going wrong.

Now, let me take you back to the beginning. Well, not right to the beginning. No-one needs to hear about me coming out of my mother's fanny.

Chapter Two

My first time with some girls (The 1990's)

I wasn't always gay you know. Well, that's not technically true. My mother always says she knew I was a homosexual from birth. Apparently, I came out doing cartwheels and singing songs from Phantom of the Opera.

Okay, so maybe I'm exaggerating that slightly but you get the gist. Another giveaway was probably stealing my sister's dolls and then crying when she wouldn't let us take it in turns to push the doll's pram.

But I've digressed here. Gone off the beaten track. Pardon the pun. Where was I? Oh yes, I'd just made the slightly untrue statement that I wasn't always gay. What is actually more truthful to say is that I wasn't always out to the world.

And I did that old trick that I'm pretty sure all gay boys are guilty of, especially from my era of the 1980s and 1990s. I pretended that I was bisexual because, to me, it made it seem less scary than saying, 'Hey I'm a fully fledged 100% penis loving homosexual!'

So in my quest to prove I wasn't a fully fledged homo and only a Bi, I decided that I would have to try a girl out for size.

I used to steal copies of The Daily Sport from the local newsagent. I was a paperboy in my youth you know. I don't for the life of me know why I stole The Daily Sport.

Well, I do actually. I was still pretending not to be a poof. So I thought stealing a paper that had tits in it made me look like a hard man to the boys on my estate. But all I was really doing was trying to impress the boys that I was actually fantasising about!

I've kissed quite a few girls in my time, I'll have you know. It was easy to stick your tongue down their throats. I just pretended it was our postman, who I fancied, or my P.E. teacher. My P.E. teacher, OH MY DAYS, I can still remember his face now.

He was a beautiful man. And he was the reason I could never stand up straight in a pair of shorts during my school years. Every time I saw him, I got a stonking great hard on and had to do my best impression of The Hunchback of Notre-Dame to hide it.

After a while though, the girls I was kissing weren't just happy with a snog anymore. We were 16 now and they wanted something other than my tongue inside them. 'Oh god', I thought. 'What was I to do?', I may have kissed them. But never had I felt a hard-on as a result.

My first attempt at sexual intercourse was with a girl called Tina. I remember it like it was yesterday. I'd sprinkled rose petals all over the bed in my attempt to make it romantic.

Yes, I know.

Rose petals.

Sheer cheese.

I'd watched too many episodes of The Bold and the Beautiful during the 1990s.

And, not surprisingly, it also had an ending like a melodramatic soap opera. We kissed. She got naked on the bed. And then I whipped my clothes off and wrapped a condom on.

Yes, I managed to get hard! I thank the Lord for my vivid imagination. Because that was not Tina on the bed. It was Tinhead from *Brookside*.

Just as I was about to make my MARK, (yes, pun intended), Tinhead, sorry I mean Tina, grabbed my arm and pushed me off.

"I'm sorry! I can't do it with you. I'm a lesbian!" Oh, the irony.

My next attempt at proving my bisexuality was with a girl called Hayley. We went camping together. My first time with a girl, under the stars, in a tent, out in a field. I thought this would be so romantic.

"As I toasted a marshmallow over the campfire for her, I felt her hand caress my thigh. I was nearly as soft and gooey as the marshmallow but along came my vivid imagination once more.

"And, as if by magic, Hayley was Hunter from *Gladiators*".

Mini Mark was poised, raised and ready for action. I felt Hayley undo my flies. My eyes nearly popped out of their sockets. If a girl touches my penis, I'll be scarred for life, I told myself.

To stop her wandering hands, and to take her attention away from my penis, I got two fingers and put them up her skirt. I heard her groan, but meanwhile, I was trying to stop myself from gagging.

I felt like I was prodding a raw fillet steak and, to this day, I always have to have my meat well cooked. My bisexual days were over.

100% Gay man had been erected. Pun definitely intended.

Chapter Three

How I came out to my parents (June 2001)

It was the summer of 2001. *Bridget Jones' Diary* had just been released at Easter and Tullene and myself had already seen it five times. Tullene was, and still is, my best friend to this day. We've been causing trouble together since we were sweet sixteen year olds. It was a few weeks until my 18th birthday and I'd just passed my driving test.

I can still remember my first car to this day. It was a Talbot. I don't even know if that make of car is still in existence. Car makes and models are not my specialist subject. It was my pride and joy though, a beautiful silver colour and I called it Toby. Toby the Talbot.

I bought it off my mum's mate, Barbara, for fifty quid. Apparently, she didn't want to charge me anything but my mother insisted she make me pay something. She was very keen on teaching me the value of money!

Many a night after the passing of my driving test, Tullene and I, along with our fellow best friends Amber and Gemma would often be found driving aimlessly around Central London.

Well, it was something to do. We clearly thought we were hard nuts.

We'd blare Destiny's Child's 'Bootylicious' from the car CD player, windows down, partying through the polluted London streets in my Toby.

I remember one particular night when we stopped at some traffic lights on Oxford Street. I hung out the window with a frying pan. (Don't ask me why we had a frying pan in the car. We were 17!) Clutching onto the random cooking utensil, I asked a woman if she fancied a fry up. I'm guessing she didn't fancy one by the disgusted look she threw my way.

The lights turned green and we sped off towards Bond Street. The woman looked at us as though we'd escaped from the asylum and we all laughed hysterically. Oh, the idiocy of youth.

I've completely digressed off the subject of my coming out story to my parents but I feel describing my beautiful Toby Talbot is important in setting the scene. He played a vital role in the story.

I was fast approaching my 18th birthday and I'd fallen in love with a boy in the year above me at college. Darren. But he's a story for a later date. I decided that before I declared my love for Darren, I had to tell my mum and dad I was gay.

I pulled up outside Tullene's house and beeped my horn. I heard Mummy Pat (Tullene's mum) shout out the window. "Keep the noise down!" Tullene came running out the house and jumped in Toby.

"We're going to see Mummy and Daddy Morgan", I told her.

"Why?"

"Tonight's the night."

Being my best friend, she knew exactly what I meant. I couldn't do it on my own. I needed Tullene by my side. And she still is by my side through most dramas, twenty years later.

Driving onto the council estate where I lived, I could feel my hands getting clammy and beads of sweat on my forehead. Yes, I could sweat back then. I was only 17 remember and hadn't a need for Botox yet.

We parked outside the back gate and Tullene went to open the passenger door.

"NOT YET!" I screamed, unnecessarily loudly. I saw her wig nearly hit the roof as she jumped as a reaction to my bellowing.

I say wig, and not head, as Tullene has a vast collection of wigs that she adorns on her scalp. She would be the envy of any drag queen. She has a hairpiece for every occasion.

"I need a cigarette to calm my nerves."

I grabbed a Marlboro light from my glove box and puffed on it like my life depended on it.

How could that 17-year-old boy afford Marlboro lights, I hear you cry? Well, this was 2001 remember and they were only £3.99 for a packet of twenty. I don't smoke any longer but I believe they are about twelve quid a pack now. I don't know how anyone affords to smoke these days.

As we sat there, chugging on a ciggy, I saw my sister Clare pull up in her car. She had a purple Fiesta which was later to become my car after Toby Talbot went up to motor vehicle heaven. And she would become Fiona Fiesta.

"What are you doing out here?" Clare enquired as she came up to say hello.

"I've got something to tell mum and dad."

"What?"

"I'm gay."

"Okay then. Let's go inside and tell them."

I lost my bottle. I quickly started the engine and swore my sister to secrecy. And then me and Tullene sped off. Driving around Central London, I heard a beep from my Nokia 3310 to indicate a text message. It soon became apparent my sister was no good at keeping secrets.

"Read the message to me Tullene."

It was from my mum.

"We still love you", it said.

And there you have it. No fanfares or whistles in this coming out story. Just a sister with a big gob.

Chapter Four

Don't offer your date a blow job to warm him up (December 2001)

T here was Jimmy. He was my first foray into internet dating. We'd met on Gaydar. All my older gays will remember this site. It was big long before Grindr came along.

Jimmy made it perfectly clear that he wanted more than just sex. He wanted us to get to know each other. I remember he worked at Tesco. So, one night, when he finished his shift, I went to pick him up in my car. I thought we could go for a romantic drive.

It was a cold winter's night, deep into December. I'd love to say it was snowing to make the story sound more romantic, but I'd be lying.

We pulled over to admire the Christmas lights on Oxford Street and I could see Jimmy was shivering.

"I'll give you a blow job to warm you up!" I blurted out. I was joking of course but Jimmy was more prudish than I'd given him credit for. And clearly lacked a sense of humour.

"How rude!" He retorted. And quickly made his excuses so that I would drop him home.

Chapter Five

The first time I had my heart broken (June 2002)

The summer of 2002. A year after I'd come out to my parents with no fanfare. It was also the year when *Sex and the City* only had EIGHT episodes in that year's season. Devastated. All because Sarah Jessica Parker was pregnant. So selfish.

Remember Darren from college? Over the past year I'd fallen head over heels in love with him. It was the first time I'd been in love. Although with the benefit of hindsight, I don't think I was truly in love. But it made my heart feel good all the same.

I remember thinking he was the most beautiful man I had ever seen. He had the most glorious mop of blonde hair and my god, he was sodding tall.

And that was the moment I had my education in the tall guy, huge cock, lesson of life. It was so wide; I could barely get my mouth round it. And for those who know me personally, know how big my gob is. Say no more.

But I digress again. I wasn't supposed to get to the tale of his penis yet. But thinking about it again, after all these years, got me all excited. And I just couldn't wait to tell you all.

Darren was the year above me at college. An older man. I was only 17 and he was 18. I felt so sophisticated bagging myself a bloke who was a whole year older than me.

To add to the sophistication and class of the situation, I got my gay best friend from college,

Kyle, to test the waters for me. I was far too shy to ask him out myself. I hadn't quite grown into my SAMANTHA confidence stakes yet.

Getting the green light from Kyle, I found myself on the most romantic date of my life. In case that doesn't translate from the page, that was sarcasm. He took me for lunch at GREGGS.

To this day, I'm still partial to a Greggs. I can never have just one item either. It always has to be a chicken tikka baguette, a pizza slice and an apple Danish. Fat fuck, I know. But I've never been obsessed with having a Muscle Mary body.

It took me a few years after Darren, before I could step inside a Greggs store without a lump in my throat and a tear in my eye. Melodramatic I know, but I was a teenage boy, in love for the first time. Forgive me.

In the afternoon after 'THAT' date, I found myself in a massive cliché. We ended up behind the bike sheds and before you could say 'steak bake', he had his tongue down my throat.

Whoever coined the phrase 'you have to kiss a few frogs before you meet your prince' was right on the money. For this bike shed fumble was exactly what I imagined kissing a frog would be like.

He clearly hadn't had enough to eat at Greggs, as he seemed to make the decision to eat half my face. His lips engulfed my lips. AND my nose. AND my cheekbones.

I surfaced from the kiss with a red raw face. It had been sucked to within an inch of its life. I thought he was about to take my face and stick it to the back window of a car. And with the amount of saliva I appeared to have on my face, even a hacksaw wouldn't have prised me off that window.

I was dating a face sucker. But I decided I could train him to keep his mouth on my lips ONLY. And besides, I idolised him.

We had a few more lunch dates in Greggs. What can I say? I'm a cheap date. And then he started inviting me round to his house when his parents went out for the night. Very illicit and teenagesque.

And this is when I came face to face with the tree trunk. AKA, his penis. I must say, for a few years after Darren had left my life, many men were a disappointment to me in the trouser department. Until I came to the realisation that Darren was an exception to most men. He had an exceptionally large manhood.

My new found love was all going swimmingly. I was planning the house we would live in, how many kids we would have and what our wedding would be like. Before anyone judges me, remember I was an 18 year old teenager, experiencing my first taste of love.

And then it all came crashing down around me. Kyle had bumped into Darren on a night out.

Darren grabbed Kyle's face and tried to kiss him. Kyle pulled away.

"I love you. Not Mark", the bastard declared. Sorry, I mean Darren.

Kyle walked away from Darren and decided he should do the decent thing and inform me immediately. He phoned me and told me he needed to see me. I went to pick him up in my Toby Talbot.

He told me of the night's events and I melodramatically

exited the car, a la *Sex and the City* style. And I cried in the street. My heart broke and as tears streamed down my face, I wondered if my heart would ever mend.

Chapter Six

Kyle and the drama exam (July 2002)

After the Kyle and Darren debacle, I thought I would never love again. I sat listening to 'How do I live without you?' by Leanne Rimes, tears dripping into my Sauvignon Blanc. Okay, so that sounds even more melodramatic, but I was a young 18 year old gay boy who had just had his heart broken for the first time. I'm allowed!

One night, the three amigos, also known as me, Tullene and Kyle were in KU bar having a blow job. That's a shot by the way. We didn't partake in acts of voyeurism.

Having downed our blow jobs, a rather handsome but very shy chap came up to us. Kyle didn't take much notice of him but he certainly caught my eye.

"I'm Travis", the boy managed to just about stutter out the words.

Kyle took absolutely no notice of Travis. He had already cast his net out to Travis's friend, Harry, who was close behind. Ignoring Travis's held out hand, Kyle pushed past it and made a beeline for Harry.

Not one for being coy or backward in coming forward our Kyle. Rejected by Harry, Kyle made Travis his consolation prize. Just as I was getting my hooks into Travis, Kyle swept in and well and truly reeled him in for himself.

Sighing, I decided another blow job was in order. Plenty more fish in the sea. And before you could say, 'Catch of the day!', Kyle and Travis had become inseparable. And when I say inseparable, I mean at the lips. It's a wonder they didn't die of asphyxiation.

Now, I love Kyle to pieces but he could be a bit of a bastard in our youth. And Travis could be a bit needy. To say they had a compatible relationship is like saying the Queen lives on a council estate.

Many a night, I would have Travis crying down the landline to me, heartbroken at Kyle's latest act. Yes, a landline. It was 2002 so mobiles to the masses were still to come.

We would talk for hours, night after night. My mum would often question if Travis was really Kyle's boyfriend.

"The amount he phones you, are you sure he's not YOUR boyfriend love?" She would yell.

I did get a flutter every time the phone rang and my mum would pick up the receiver of our slimline telephone. I'd run to the top of the stairs, praying my mother would shout up and tell me the call was mine.

But I knew the feelings weren't reciprocated. Travis was smitten with Kyle and just needed a friend. And I was more than happy to the play the part of his confidant.

A few months into their tumultuous relationship, the whole of our Performing Arts A-level class was out dancing the night away in G-A-Y. Many an ill spent night of our teenage years was in there.

"You bastard!" We all heard Travis scream. It didn't take a genius to work out exactly to whom he was referring. Kyle decided to leave us all behind and trot off down Tottenham Court Road. So, we were left to deal with his boyfriend. He obviously thought this was the best course of action. It may have been for him, but we had a wailing Travis to contend with, snot ridden nose to boot.

It was left to Lucy and myself to pick up the pieces. Lucy, Kyle's best friend, had a big gob; no different to the rest of us. Anyway, she suggested we take Travis back to her house and then we could decide what to do in the morning.

Making us up a little bed on her floor, Lucy fell into her King size mattress and left us to sleep. Although little sleeping went on...

Still drunk and emotional, Travis put his arms around me for comfort as we shut our eyes for the night. Feeling his vodka-soaked breath on my face gave me flutters. And I'm not talking about in my heart.

I took a sharp intake of breath and opened my eyes, to be greeted with Travis just staring at me. Feeling awkward, I managed a grin and then we had a moment.

Our lips edged closer together and we shared a passionate kiss. My stomach flipped and as for my penis; he thought all his Christmases and birthdays had come at once. Putting my hand down the front of Travis's trousers was disturbed by Lucy's foghorn.

"STOP! Both of you. Kyle is your boyfriend. And he's your friend."

Acting sheepishly, we decided it would be best if I jumped in with Lucy for the rest of the night. And then there was silence. None of us spoke about it. Until two days later...

Cue the most dramatic A-level drama exam in history.

I'm sure it will come as no surprise that Tullene, Kyle and myself were all taking Performing Arts as our main subject at college. We were all pretty damn good at it, even if I do say so myself. Although it didn't take much work; we were all drama queens.

But this was it. Our final exam. Our final ever day at college together. And then we would be thrown out into the big bad world. Some of us were going off to university, some of us straight into jobs.

But not before one last big announcement from Kyle. Smack bang in the middle of my soliloquy.

That fateful night between Travis and me had not been mentioned since. Or so I thought. Obviously, I told Tullene immediately. We tell each other everything. Even to this day.

Just as I was nearing the end of my best impersonation of Hamlet, Kyle stood up, quite unexpectedly.

"Some people can't get their own boyfriends", he declared.

I gulped. So did Tullene. You could have heard a pin drop. Our tutor's eyes lit up. Bored drama exams, I think she was secretly sending a prayer up, thanking the Lord for the interruption. You could almost see her lips salivating at the scandal.

Never one to do things by halves, Kyle didn't stop there.

"Some people can't get their own boyfriends so they have to go after other people's. Don't they Mark?"

I wanted the ground to swallow me up. Kyle walked out to the sound of 'Doof Doof.' Okay, so I made that bit up. No one played the EastEnders theme tune.

I never saw or heard from Travis again. Well, not until three years later...

Chapter Seven

Don't Let Your Best Friend's Mum Choose Your Dates (September 2002)

He looked like Roy Cropper; it was never going to work out.

I've had a flashback to a date I went on when I was just a young whippersnapper of 19. My first foray into dating after Darren dumped me for my gay best friend.

Christ, that means I've been undateable for a total of.... well, a long time. Almost 21 years. Yes, I hear the sound of your shocked voices. That man can't be 40! But yes, I am. It's amazing what a bit of exfoliation can do for your skin. Oh, and not forgetting the needle full of Botox I regularly get pricked with. Well, I have to get a prick from somewhere. (Clears throat)

Anyway...

Back to my flashback which takes us back to the wonderful year of 2002. The year that bought us the Queen's Golden Jubilee and Girls Aloud! The latter being my most memorable and personal favourite. But back to something else that wasn't my particularly most favourite memory of that year, the date that was organised by my friend's 50-year-old mum.

So, there I was this one morning, having coffee with Gwen. I mean, she isn't the most sane of people you'll ever meet, but I've had my fair share of mental institute moments over the years, so who am I to judge? As I took a sip on my mocha. I'm sure I would have been drinking a mocha. It's only since I've hit my 30s have I become partial to an espresso. So, as I sipped the mocha, she announced she'd set me up on a date with this lovely man she worked with on check in.

An airport worker.

Now, my dear Nan, God rest her soul, taught me I should never sit in judgement of others. But sometimes I find that piece of advice very hard to swallow. For some reason, in my sinful judgemental mind, I associate anyone working at the airport as a slag and having a man in every country. I know my face needs a slap as obviously he only works on check in, so unless he has a very long lunch break, I rationalise that he can't make it to other countries.

After giving my chops a quick swift slap, I took in the details of the date. It was that coming Saturday, at 7pm and I was to meet him at the Birdcage. Cor, the Birdcage in Chiswick, now that is showing my age. As I took the final chocolatey sip of my mocha, she threw the final, and possibly most vital, piece of information at me.

My new date was 50-years-old. My jaw slapped the ground like a concrete slab thrown from the top of Big Ben.

As I looked in the mirror at my fresh, youthful, wrinkle free face, I told myself age is but a number. I mean, what does it matter that he's 31 years older than me? Not a problem. He could be the man of my dreams, I shouldn't be ageist, I told myself. As the stark realisation dawned on me that he's the same age as my dad, I began to gag, but a shot of vodka and a Marlboro Light soon slapped that image out of me.

I walked up to the bar of the Birdcage. Unfashionably early, purely because my best friend booted me out the car as she wanted to get back to see the Pop Idol final. I ordered a pint of Fosters. I decided beer is the best drink for me to consume that evening, it gets me less pissed and as I was dealing with a senior citizen; I wanted to keep my wits about me. I grabbed my pint and took myself to a small round table and perched myself on a bar stool.

As I finished off my first pint of Fosters, a man with a shopping bag approached me. He asked me a question but my eyes were firmly placed on his shopping bag. Had Roy Cropper just walked in? (For those of you who have never seen Coronation Street, Google this man and you will have the image of my date).

Let's call my date Roy from now on, as his actual name escapes me. Call it the early onset of Alzheimer's, or even just my own mind's ability to block it out. As this is a date I have tried to forget all through my twenties. And it's also the date that set the precedent: never let your friend's mum set you up on a date.

Now I wouldn't have minded being on a date with a 50-year-old, had Roy not acted and looked like he was 75! I know I'm partial to being a little dramatic, but on this occasion, I really don't think I am being. I mean, the shopping bag said it all! He bought me a pint of Fosters, so that's a point in his favour but I needed another one to block out the dull tone of his voice as he discussed trains and planes that he liked to spot. Wonderful, I'm sat with a train spotter. I really should have remembered to cross dear old Gwen off my Christmas card list. But I don't like to think of myself as a bitter old queen.

Five pints of fosters later (all bought by Roy, may I add), and I was somewhat tipsy. I noticed his body language. He started to touch my hand, then my arm. He must have thought all his

Christmases had come at once. This young pretty boy sat in front of him, pissed on Fosters, who needed looking after. After the sixth pint (also bought by Roy), I started to feel myself returning his body language gestures. A metaphoric slap later and I was in the toilet, on the phone to Tullene.

"You must pick me up!" I pleaded with her.

"But the winner of Pop Idol hadn't been announced yet." Came her reply.

"Oh, don't worry about your best friend, sat here, about to be taken advantage of by Roy Cropper", I barked back.

Luckily for me, I heard Girls Aloud announced the winners, so she left her house to rescue me. Whoever thought I'd owe Cheryl Cole for saving me from Roy Cropper?

As I returned to the table, I saw my seventh pint of fosters slammed down on the table by Roy.

Phew! I've made the right call by phoning my best friend, pardon the pun. I saw the intentions in Roy's eyes. Glistening like a magpie who's just seen a diamond ring. Just as I picked up the fosters, my best friend ran in, like the hero of the hour.

"You must come quickly! My mum's been taken ill and I need you!" She screamed.

Oh, the lies and drama of the youth.

I looked at Roy, feigning upset.

"I'm so sorry, but I must go!"

"Will I see you again?" Roy was like a lost puppy dog.

The lies of the youth continued rolling out of my mouth like a red carpet at the Oscars.

"Of course, give me call. I've had a really lovely evening!"

I'm going straight to hell, I told myself.

My best friend dragged me from the Birdcage, and I noticed Donna Summers had started playing. I joined in on the chorus, rather loudly and as we left, Roy was following us. I turned around, and in my Fosters induced state, I sang at him, at the top of my lungs:

"Enough is enough is enough, I can't go on, I can't go on no more, no!"

Chapter Eight

Losing my V-plates (February 2003)

I'd kissed many frogs. Sucked a few cocks. And given many a hand shandy. But I still hadn't gone the whole way.

No man had put his sausage up my back alley. And my chipolata had not graced itself between any man's cheeks. I didn't even know what position I was. A top? A bottom? Or would I be versatile?

Enter Seb. The love of my life so far. We lasted just over a year and it was certainly a fiery relationship.

I remember one heated argument at a petrol station after my car had broken down. Seb, Tullene and I were out on a drive in the country when the car just stopped. Luckily, we were just up the road from a garage so we managed to get out and push ourselves up the lane.

Well, I say we. It was all performed by Tullene and me. Seb was camper than a row of tents and the heaviest object he could ever pick up was his mascara wand. But I loved him, so it didn't matter.

As we all sat outside Esso, (I can't actually remember if it was an Esso but that's the first garage name that popped into my head), Seb started annoying me. God knows what he had done. He didn't always need a reason. Just the fact he was breathing would sometimes piss me off.

I get this trait from my mother. My dad's only got to cough and she'll flip her lid. It's called love apparently.

Waiting for the AA to come and rescue us, Seb continued breathing so our argument ensued. I could see Tullene's nostrils start to flare which is a warning sign she's getting pissed off.

"If you two are going to carry on, can you just get out the car!!" She screamed.

You do as you're told when Tullene starts shouting, so obediently we got out the car and the dramatic disagreement continued on the forecourt.

Seeing the bright yellow AA van pulling up next to us, Tullene jumped out of the car, ready to kiss the mechanic for rescuing her from the situation.

The mechanic was rather dishy, and Seb didn't fail to notice his dashing good looks. Just to wind me up a bit more, he started flirting with the grease ridden rescuer.

It was my turn to flare the nostrils and, being an irrational and jealous 19 year old, I couldn't control my anger.

"Why don't you just ask him to stick his tool in your bonnet?" I cried out.

Tullene, embarrassed, grabbed my arm. I say grabbed; it was more of a grip with nails digging in.

"STOP IT! You're sounding nutty."

Before you could shout, OIL CHANGE, Seb had jumped on my back to try and make light of the situation. I was in no mood to be giving him a piggy back. I was like a wild thing, flinging him about, trying to push him off my back, but to no avail.

We were causing quite a scene by this time and the mechanic

looked like he might just drive off and leave us to fend for ourselves.

Seb went to bite my ear as the engine revved up. Tullene kissed the mechanic to express her gratitude at getting the motor going again.

"Now get in the car!" She bellowed, and never came on a drive in the country with us again.

That night, I think the passion of the petrol station fight had made us a bit horny.

We had been together six weeks now and decided tonight was the night that we would make love. Yes, MAKE LOVE. I was still a naïve young gay boy. I'd decided that I wanted to lose my virginity once I was in love. And besides the forecourt ear biting extravaganza, I was definitely in love.

Lying in bed, bare flesh on bare flesh, we lovingly looked at each other. I took his face in my hands.

"I want to be inside you", I beamed.

"I want to be inside you", he beamed back.

AWKWARD. By this time, I had decided I wanted to be a top. I couldn't imagine having anything up my bum. At the risk of sounding homophobic, I'd reached the conclusion my arse was an exit only. And besides, having been diagnosed with IBS at 16, I was terrified of shitting all over the man.

Before you could mutter the words, POP MY CHERRY, I was making love to Seb. I'd won the battle and taken the TOP prize. Pun intended.

Chapter Nine

That time I got pissed on (August 2003)

The year Mark Haddon's novel "The Curious Incident of the Dog in the Night-Time" was published. The year Dirty Den made his comeback in EastEnders. And the year Jemini entered the Eurovision Song Contest with "Cry Baby." The song which gained the worst placing ever for the United Kingdom. I personally quite like the song. It's even on my iPod to this day.

It was also the year when I still considered myself to be dateable. I had been with my current boyfriend for almost six months and I was head over heels in love. I thought I was going to marry this man, Seb. One of the only men I have truly loved in my life.

We first met when I was still a customer service manager for Budgens' supermarket and he worked in the hairdressers two doors down. I would often walk past the salon, slyly looking through the window using only my peripheral vision. And more often than not, I would see him staring back at me. And then I would feel my heart flutter inside my chest.

SHEER CHEESE, I know, but I was still a hopeless romantic

back then. Years of unsuccessful dating hadn't yet made me bitter or cynical.

One day, I finally plucked up the courage to ask him out. Well, I say I plucked up the courage. What actually happened was that I made Tullene go inside the salon to hand him a piece of paper. On said piece of paper, I had written my phone number.

That night, I was pissed in the local pub. Quelle Surprise! And up popped a text. Yes, a text. Not a WhatsApp. It was 2003 remember. It was from the hairdresser of my dreams. I was so excited and almost hyperventilated. Tullene had to give me a little slap. And she actually did. Sadistic bitch.

Before I knew it, I was in G-A-Y at the Astoria on a date! YES, The Astoria! Oh my god. How I miss that place. All through my late teens and right into my twenties, I would spend Thursday, Friday and Saturday nights in there, dancing the night away. I look back and I think, 'how on earth did I afford to be out that much?' And then I remember double vodkas were only £1.50 and you could get a blow job for a quid.

No, you youngsters reading, prostitutes were not that cheap back in 2003. A Blow Job was a delicious shot available in many gay venues. It may well still be in this day and age but my clubbing days are over, so I'm less informed of the shot menu of gay establishments.

For those who have never had a Blow Job, make one at home. Pour Amaretto in the base of a shot glass and top with coffee liqueur. Layer Irish Cream on top of that and then squirt on some whipped cream. Delicious! I might actually make one tonight now. It will certainly be the first blow job I've had in a while. Cue violins.

Anyway, I've digressed. This is meant to be a tale of being pissed ON, and not actually being PISSED.

After six months of sheer cheesy love and romance, I decided it was time Seb and I took a mini-break. So off we went down to my favourite place in the whole of the United Kingdom - West Wittering.

Driving along the A3, "Crazy in Love" by Beyoncé blaring from the speakers, windows down and the wind blowing through our hair. Yes, I still had hair back then too. I hadn't succumbed to the fate of my Dad's gene pool quite yet.

And out of nowhere, the wind lifted the baseball cap from my bonce and we saw it blowing away down the A3, back towards London. Very Bridget Jones-esque.

Lying on the beach, sand between our toes and the sea glistening in the August sunshine, I looked across at my perfect boyfriend and held his hand. I had never felt so happy. I was still a naïve 19-year-old and now, almost twenty years later, I can see it was never going to end happily. But hindsight is a wonderful tool.

To end the peace and romance of the moment, Seb suddenly screamed.

"OH MY GOD! It's a Jellyfish!"

And all of a sudden, I felt a large splat on my chest. The bastard had thrown it at me. Jumping up, I screamed.

"YOU IDIOT!"

I saw seaweed fall from my chest to the sand below. It had been a practical joke.

Within seconds, I had returned the joke by flinging seaweed at his face (yes, his face. No half measures for me, I go straight for the jugular!) I screamed,

"JELLYFISH!"

His camp scream and running, well, mincing actually, off down the sand made it all worthwhile. A few minutes later, I felt another splat against my chest. Within a few seconds, I felt an intense stinging. As the culprit slipped from my chest, it was clear to see it was an ACTUAL Jellyfish this time.

"You Prick!" I bellowed as I began to go red and blotchy.

We went up to the shop, desperate to find some E45. But, not surprisingly, the beach shop didn't stock it as part of their product range.

"I could piss on you", Seb suggested.

"Now is not the time or place to begin acting out your sexual fantasies!" I retorted.

He reassured me that urine is apparently a good ointment to deal with a Jellyfish sting. And as this was 2003, I didn't have the luxury of Google on my Nokia 3310 to support his claims.

Desperate, red, itchy, and stinging, I threw myself to the floor, well hidden behind my car and Seb whapped his cock out. Before I knew it, my chest was being used as a urinal.

Chapter Ten

That time my boyfriend gave me crabs
(December 2003)

After being together a whole eleven months, things between Seb and I started to become quite fraught. Luckily, both ears were still intact.

I'm reminiscing about an era in my early twenties. Back when Atomic Kitten and Destiny's Child were ruling the charts. A time when I dreamed of a sex change to become Tanya Turner and marry a footballer.

But as usual, I'm digressing and babbling on without getting to the point. Maybe that's what I do on first dates and why I've rarely made it to a second date. Anyway, I'm not here for self-analysis.

I was so in love with this boy in my early twenties. And he was so in love with me. Now I think about it, his name, Sebastian, was an unfortunate choice for his parents to give him, considering this is a tale of crabs, and I'm not talking about the cute red one from The Little Mermaid.

For nearly a year we lived in each other's pockets, a whirl-wind romance. I thought to myself on a daily basis; This is a man

I'm going to spend the rest of my life with. He even met my family which is a rarity in my love life.

And then one night, I remember this vividly like it was only yesterday.

I was having a glass of wine with Jane, my neighbour, and I saw her staring peculiarly at my crotch. Feeling I may need to remind her I'm gay, she suddenly screamed,

"You've been itching all night!"

After another glass of wine, I plucked up the courage to pull my trousers down in front of a lady. Well, I don't know if you can call Jane a lady but let's use that word because I'm feeling quite nice as I write this.

As she examined my pubic region, I heard her scream as she came eye to eye with a crab. Our jaws dropped and I burst into tears.

So did Jane, I think.

We pulled out a medical dictionary from the bookshelf. Yes, that's right. And from said dictionary, we self-diagnosed crabs. I pulled one out and I could see it's legs moving. Probably the most unpleasant moment of my life. Oh, and probably Janes' as well.

A quick visit to the sexual health clinic confirmed the self-diagnosis as correct. But the bare-faced cheek of the doctor asking me if I knew the dangers of sleeping around.

"I've got a boyfriend who I've been with for over a year!" I bellowed.

"Well, one of you has been a naughty boy!" She retorted.

After establishing that it's very rare to catch crabs from a toilet seat or dirty bedding, my eyes widened as I drew the only plausible conclusion. Sebastian must have been cheating on me, because I damn well knew I had followed the rules of my Christian upbringing and remained faithful.

A few panic attack's later and a slap around the face for

Sebastian, another realisation dawned on me. I had to tell my Mum and Dad. The doctor had told me that everything in my house needed to go in the washing machine on a hot wash. And I still lived with my parents. Oh, the sheer embarrassment.

And then my eyes widened even wider at the prospect I may have given my Mum and Dad crabs. Our towels were always hanging on the rail together. Luckily, this story has a happy ending.

Sebastian was given his marching orders. But not until one final showdown a few weeks later.

I got rid of my infestation.

And my parents were crab free.

Chapter Eleven

When your New Year's Eve goes off with a bang... (New Year's Eve 2003)

I'd just turned 20 and I'd dumped the love of my life because he gave me crabs. I thought we were going to be together forever. Oh, the naivety of youth.

I was still customer service manager for Budgens Supermarket back in those days. Good old Budgens. You rarely see them around on the high street these days.

A few weeks before my boyfriend had given me the itch, I'd bought him a brand new mobile phone worth £150! Now, that was a lot of money back in those days. God, I'm starting to sound like me Nan. God rest her soul.

I can remember the moment of my realisation as vividly as if it were yesterday. He still had his bloody mitts on the £150 phone. I was having none of it. There was no way he was keeping it. So, I marched down to the hairdressers where he worked, two doors down from Budgens.

As I barged my way through the doors, I was greeted by a salon full of ladies having their blow dries, all getting ready to look glamorous to celebrate the New Year. But I didn't care. I was still heartbroken and acting irrationally. Only five minutes before, I'd been in tears down the fruit and veg aisle as 'All I want for Christmas' played over the tannoy.

I bellowed to make myself heard over the hair dryers and as I did, I saw the salon manager making her way towards me.

"I WANT THE PHONE BACK!" I barked as I held my hand out to Seb. You could see the client's eyes all lighting up as the hairdresser's scorned ex made a scene. It was giving them all a juicy bit of gossip that they could share over a glass of champagne that evening.

"Mark! This is not the time or the place!"

"Just hand over the phone and I'll leave!"

He handed it over alright, desperate to get rid of me from the salon.

Back in the safety of my office in Budgens, I had itchy fingers as I clutched the phone. I was battling with my conscience. Should I read his messages or not? The devil on my shoulder won the battle.

As I clicked open on the inbox, my eyebrows raised. Yes, I can promise you they did. It was the days before I started having Botox. And my jaw dropped to the desk.

I witnessed many explicit messages between my ex and another man. All dating back to when we were still together! Part of me wished I'd never looked and the other part of me was glad I had. Although they do say ignorance is bliss.

I slammed the phone down on the desk as steam erupted from my ears. I looked up at the clock. 6pm. The salon would be closing. I decided I had to have it out with my ex. How dare he be sexting and seeing another man when we were still together. This was the evidence I needed. Bastard. I was so angry; I could have crushed a grape.

I peeped my head out of Budgens' front door and I could see

the salon was already in darkness. I knew he'd be waiting at the bus stop. I simply had to have it out with him. There was no way I was going into 2004 without dealing with this.

"JANE!" I screamed as I saw her filling up the shelves with Hovis loaves. She jumped to attention. Jane, bless her, and for her sins, was not only my neighbour but one of my staff at Budgens.. There was an incident once where she threw some Hovis loaves at me during an argument we were having. But I'll save that story for another time.

"Please drive me to the bus stop!" I pleaded with her. She grabbed her car keys and we made a swift exit out of the supermarket doors. She screeched to a halt at the bus stop and I saw my ex gulp as I slammed the door shut and walk towards him.

In the meantime, Jane could sense I was about to start a cat-fight so she jumped out of the car as quickly as she could. But in her haste, her foot got caught in her seat belt and she went face first into the gutter.

As she scrambled back onto her feet, I had my hand raised ready to make my first move on my cheating ex. I slapped his face, a la Pat Butcher and Peggy Mitchell style. I took a deep breath and I started to make my way back towards the car. In my mind, a slap had brought the matter to a close.

But clearly my ex had different ideas, and before I knew it, I felt a foot up my backside and I went down to the pavement like a sack of shit. Onto my knees I fell as he kicked me up the derriere.

Too many years of watching Dynasty had prepared me for my next move in the inevitable cat-fight that was about to ensue.

I leapt from my knees like a pouncing tiger and jumped onto his back. We both hit the pavement like a sack of spuds and started to roll around, limp wrists clawing at each other, with no decorum whatsoever.

As we took it in turns to be on top (a first time for everything as he was always very selfish when it came to that normally), I saw out the corner of my eye that quite a crowd was beginning to gather around us.

"Look at Krystle and Alexis!" I heard a bystander call out. Being such a Dynasty fan, I oozed with pride. And hoped I was Alexis. Well, I prayed pretty hard actually.

When Jane could see that there was going to be no outright winner of the cat-fight, she dragged us apart screaming.

"ENOUGH!" For anyone who doesn't know Jane, let me tell you, she's rather scary. She would be very good in the cast of Wentworth Prison. So, me and the ex jumped to attention and got back onto our feet rather quickly.

Doing her best headmistress impression, Jane had a good grip on my arm. I assume it was to make sure I didn't make a break for it and dish out another slap. She opened the car door and practically threw me into the passenger seat.

I couldn't bear not to have the last word, so as Jane started the engine, I wound down my window and stuck my head out into the cold winter air.

"HAPPY NEW YEAR!" I bellowed towards my ex. Jane sped off quicker than her usual speed.

Chapter Twelve

That time I bashed the bishop (December 2004)

I t took a very long time to get over Seb. Many bottles of wine were consumed, many cigarettes smoked and many men shagged but I got there in the end. And I was finally ready to date again.

Working in Budgens always provided me with plenty of eye candy. All of the evening and weekend staff were mainly students of the male variety, all looking to earn their beer money. And I was their boss. What a fantasy.

Now, before anyone gets on the phone to the police, may I remind you that I am talking in the past tense. I was only 20 at the time of these fantasies about young male students aged 17 or 18 so it was all perfectly legal. And does not make me a sexual predator.

I always remember good old James Foster. He was the store manager. Knowing I was partial to perving on the pretty boy employees, he would often give me his words of wisdom. "Don't poke the payroll."

Being a good, obedient boy, I always listened to his advice.

Always, that was, until Adam came along. I finally had a fellow gay boy in the store.

Adam was absolutely gorgeous. He had the most beautiful blonde hair and sparkling blue eyes. And you could see his well-toned physique through his chequered green Budgens uniform. I quite often did an impression of a dog's tongue hanging out, dribbling every time I saw he was rostered on my shifts.

One night as we were filling up the shelves with loaves of Hovis, I felt our eyes meet across a thick cut granary. Unusually coy, I blushed and looked down at a white bloomer.

It was Christmas Eve and my ears caught a glimpse of George Michael in his Wham years, playing in the background. As the words of "Last Christmas" resonated in my lug holes, I took the bull by the horns.

"Would you like to go for a drink this evening?"

I looked at a Best of Both loaf to avoid making eye contact, fearful that his answer might be no.

My confidence with men in those days wasn't what it is these days. I was quite a chubby youth with a bit of acne and a fake tan addiction. I also had eyebrows that I would shave with a Bic razor which sometimes made me look like I was sporting a pair of slugs above my eyes.

My friends often say I'm the ugly duckling who blossomed into the swan. And to be honest, I'm glad I grew into my looks at a later age. All the pretty boys who I fancied in my teens at school are dog rough nowadays. So, I'm glad I went the opposite way! Better to be like a fine wine and get better with age.

Anyway, I'm digressing. Back to the drinks proposal with the medium cut Kingsmill as our witness.

"Yes." He replied rather quickly actually. Expecting the answer to be no, I didn't let my ears register the answer and started babbling on like a banshee.

"I mean, I understand if you don't want to."

"Yes!" He said again, but in my banshee induced state I continued not registering his response.

"I know it's Christmas Eve, so I completely get if you've already got plans."

And then, quite out of the blue, and I guess to shut me up, I felt him face plant his lips onto mine. All down the bakery aisle in Budgens in the year 2004. Very modern for the era, let me tell you, and no one even raised an eyebrow.

"I'll meet you at the Crossroads at 7", he said as he departed from my lips. Oh, the Crossroads. That takes me back as well. That was the pub at the end of Shepperton high street. It was our local haunt.

R.I.P Crossroads. (And I'm not talking about the dodgy ITV soap. Although that's also very sad that it's no longer around) But right now, I'm talking about the Shepperton pub which got knocked down years ago to make way for retirement homes. I miss it. Many a drunken night (or business lunch) was spent in there. Well, I say 'business' lunch. It was just an excuse for the managers to get pissed during work hours.

As we stumbled from the pub that night, we walked arm in arm and I was as pissed as a fart, I can tell you. We came to my local church and I clocked the time. Midnight Mass was about to begin.

I made the suggestion that we should attend and I could see the hesitant look on Adam's face. But I gave him a flutter of my rather long eyelashes and, before you could say "Hallelujah", we were inside the church.

We tripped our way through the doorway in our inebriated state and the first carol was already in progress. Any fellow bible bashers will know which carol we entered to. "ONCE IN

ROYAL DAVID'S CITY". It's always the first carol to be sang at Midnight mass.

I used to be in the church choir as a young boy you know. I would always sing the first verse as a solo at Midnight Mass. I had a lovely little soprano voice back in the day. Until nature came along and made my balls drop, that is.

Talking of the church choir, my mum is still in the choir to this day. And I saw her on this night; she looked up from her hymn book as she caught a glimpse of me from the choir stalls.

I could see her disapproving stare and head shake as we tumbled our way to our seats. A stare and head shake that only a mother can perfect. She could tell I was rather trollied. I knew I would be in for it on Christmas Day morning. But the Sauvignon Blanc erased any worries of her wrath right away.

This particular night, the service was being taken by the Bishop of London no less. It was a big honour for a small church in Shepperton. So, as such, it was packed to the rafters.

We were at the part of the service called the Peace. For those of you not familiar with church service proceedings, this is the when the priest invites the congregation to share God's peace with one another. And you all shake hands with each other and declare, "Peace be with you!"

As the Bishop made his way towards Adam and I, I quickly made a beeline for him, hand held out with excitement at the fact I was about to shake hands with the Bishop of London.

And in my overzealousness, I forgot to check what my feet were doing. Before I knew it, my foot became caught on the chair leg and I went face first into the Bishop's chest. My boat race smacked into the cross hanging around his neck.

As I clung onto the Bishop's hips, I felt him go a bit wobbly on his pins, and as he went backwards towards the floor, he managed to steady himself on the side of a chair.

I looked up at him, big drunken gin on my face, sorry, I meant grin, and I proudly pronounced "Peace be with you!"

He quickly peeled my body away from his hips and chest and moved onto the next member of the congregation, fearful for his life and his balance.

My mum hid herself behind her hymn book. Adam hid himself behind a pillar and pretended he was there worshipping with another group of people.

After bashing the bishop at midnight mass, I decided I would take James Foster's advice in future and not poke the payroll. Business and pleasure don't mix.

Chapter Thirteen

You slag! (January 2005)

When it comes to sex, I've always found myself to be plain and simple. Not boring; I would like to point that out immediately. But I'm not one for these chains and whips activities. Sorry Rihanna.

I mean, I've got nothing against anyone who chooses a slightly kinkier sex life than me. Each to their own, that's what I always say. It's just not my cup of tea. Or should I say a pot of freshly brewed coffee? I know it's very unBritish of me, but I can't stand tea.

I think my dislike for tea stems back to my childhood. At the risk of sounding Freudian, I blame my dad. Until I was seven, my mum would always serve me a bottle of tea every afternoon. Yes, I know. A bottle. At seven years of age. Perhaps that's where my oral capabilities come from. Years of sucking on a bottle, drinking my brew.

But one day, my father got home from work and he demanded that my mother throw my bottle away. From that day in the early 1990s, I've never touched a drop of PG Tips again.

My boyfriend Seb used to demand I call him a slag whilst making love to him. Had me screaming, "you slag!", he did. Little did I know that he was sleeping with half of London behind my back. Ironically, he was making me speak the truth. Maybe that was his way of absolution.

Chapter Fourteen

Mi amante espanol TRANSLATION- My Spanish lover (February 2005)

T aking heed of James Foster's advice of not poking the payroll, I turned my attention to the customers instead. And one particular shopper caught my eye.

Enter work best friend, Lynne. She was also my deputy. God knows who decided to let us loose together. A mincing homo who behaved like a dog on heat and a middle-aged Welsh woman who thought sophisticated dining was pie and mash. But somehow it worked and we had those checkouts running like clockwork.

One particular morning whilst Lynne was doing a price check on a cabbage, a tall, dark and suave looking man came up to browse the fruit and veg. Lynne clocked him straight away and forgetting her cabbage, she immediately called me over the tannoy.

"Mark to the fruit and veg aisle please. Spillage."

Knowing this was our code word for a FITTY, I quickly flicked my Marlboro light and made my way to the aisle as fast as my little gay trotters could carry me.

I came face to face with my Latino, just as he was groping a carrot.

DING FUCKING DONG!

Our eyes met over the top of the root vegetable and I found it disturbingly arousing the way he was handling it. We both smiled, rather coyly and shared an awkward silence.

"Can I help you sir?"

He stared at me like I'd just spoken a foreign language. I looked down to the floor. Then back up at the carrot. Then back down to the floor. No answer.

"Hello?!!" My sarcasm knows no bounds.

"Me. Speak no English. Espanol."

So, I had just spoken a foreign language. My Latino lover put the carrot in his basket and nodding his head, he carried on filling his basket with fruit and veg. As I walked off to find Lynne, I stopped to look back. And my Spanish friend had done the same. Our eyes met once more as he was fondling some figs.

"I'm in love!" I declared as Lynne and I sat down for lunch.

"You won't ever be able to understand each other. How will you hold a conversation?"

"Even better", I mused, "who needs to talk?"

"You're a slut. No wonder you can't find the love of your life." She went in for a low blow.

It was handbags at dawn time. Lynne and I loved each other unconditionally but we didn't half know how to rub each other up the wrong way. Pushing my empty dinner plate dramatically across the table, I stood up.

"Don't talk to me for the rest of the day."

"Thank God!" Lynne continued pushing my buttons. "My ears will get a rest."

"You make me so mad. I could crush a grape!" I was searching for the right insult but failed miserably.

"What are you going to do? Stab me with your mascara wand?" She always thought she was hilarious.

Walking away from Lynne before I performed an act of violence with my waterproof Maybelline, I headed down to the local bookshop. And found myself a Spanish phrasebook. I was going to learn how to communicate with my new Mediterranean hunk.

I didn't see him again for a few days which gave me plenty of time to polish up on my Holas and Que tals. I had even learnt how to say you are very handsome. Can I take you out for a drink? Or so I thought...

This one particular afternoon, I was on a health kick and had decided to give up the cigarettes. I had tried numerous times before but never lasted more than three days.

It was a very busy day on the checkouts and the girls were constantly picking up the tannoy, calling me to the tills.

"For fucks sake!" I screamed rather loudly after the third call from Lynne.

"What is it?" I grunted as I made my way to checkout four.

"Someone give him a fucking fag before I kill him!" I heard Lynne bark, deliberately loud so I could overhear.

And with that, I flounced up to the kiosk.

"Twenty Marlboro lights please." I'll try and give up again next week, I thought.

As I puffed and inhaled on my cancer stick, I noticed Mr Spain looking my way from a bench outside Budgens. Taking a deep breath, I stuck my chest out and walked towards him with sheer confidence.

"Hola!" I beamed. Taken aback at my new found language skills, he replied.

"Hola! Que tal?"

I racked my brains at how to answer and it came to me like a lightning bolt.

"Muy bien. Y usted?"

"Maravilloso." I was certain that meant marvellous. Deciding I must know his name, I continued on in my new found mother tongue.

"Como te llamas?"

"Me llamo Mateo."

I swooned on the spot. MATEO. What a name.

"Eres muy guapo." I told him he was very handsome. Speaking Spanish gave me untold confidence. I noticed him blushing.

"Gracias. Tu Tambien." OH MY GOD. He reciprocated the compliment. He thought I was handsome too. This was my chance. Ask him for a drink, a voice in my head said. And in the words of RuPaul. "And don't fuck it up." Which I did.

Instead of asking him out for a drink...

"Te gustaria ir a tomar algo?"

I asked him if he would like it up the bum.

"Te gustaria que se subiera al tresero??"

I think my Spanish needs some work.

Feeling incredibly proud, I was smiling like a Cheshire cat which probably didn't help the situation. It made me look like a psychotic sexual predator. But in my defence, I had thought I'd asked him out on a date.

Standing up, Mateo looked on at me, a little disgusted.

"No. No soy gay." Well, I didn't need my Spanish phrase book to translate that. As I embarrassingly lit another Marlboro light, Mateo, my STRAIGHT Spanish non-lover, stood up and hurriedly paced away from me down Shepperton high street. And we never saw him in Budgens again. Chucking my phrase book into the bin and stubbing out my fag, I chuckled to myself as I re-entered the store.

Noticing some rubbish on the front mat, I bent over to pick it up. As I leant over to throw it in the bin, I accidentally knocked into a trolley on its way into Budgens to do a shop. Obviously, it had a customer attached. It wasn't just a runaway trolley.

I looked up to see the owner of the piece of shopping equipment. It was Travis. Now that was a blast from the past.

Doing my best impression of a puffer fish, I was lost for words. Yes, it does occasionally happen.

"Mark. How are you?" Travis spoke first.

"Good. Just. Erm. Just. Erm. Picking up some rubbish."

"I can see."

Awkward silence alert. Which I broke. And then wished I hadn't.

"So, long time, no see. Not since I nearly put my willy up your bum on Lucy's bedroom floor."

Why the hell did I just say that? I wanted the ground to swallow me instantly. Noticing my embarrassment, Travis was chuckling to himself.

"I've thought about you a lot over the last few years. Let me take you out for a drink? We can catch up."

Well, what a turnabout of events. Not ten minutes ago, I thought I would be the one asking that question. But in Spanish. And not to Travis. I gave him my phone number and he promised to arrange. I watched him as he pushed his trolley towards the bakery department.

Chapter Fifteen

You slapper (April 2005)

I met a man who used to like to slap me during sex. Now before anyone becomes concerned for my safety and calls the police, it was only playful slaps across the boat race.

It did very little for my sex drive but it seemed to turn him on no end.

I could cope with a little slap every now and then but one day he started to scratch my back in the heat of the moment. Now scratching was still fine with me. I mean, I'd be left with a few red lines down my back for a day or two but there was no lasting damage.

But then one day, the teeth came out to play. And I'm not just talking around the neck like most normal people. The biting got so bad that I had to take to wearing roll neck jumpers, long sleeve tops, and gloves to cover up the bite marks. So I made the suggestion that he find a fellow gay who enjoys Odaxelagnia.

For those who can't be bothered to google that word:

Odaxelagnia is being sexually aroused through biting, or being bitten. It's also considered a mild form of sadism.

Chapter Sixteen

Going Speed Dating (June 2005)

S ix months after bumping into Travis and his trolley, the promised date had never come to fruition. Tired of waiting for him to make a move, I got on a tube and went speed dating.

I don't know why I hadn't thought of it years before. I'd tried Grindr, Plenty of Fish and various other dating apps. I'd attempted blind dates, set up by well-meaning friends. I'd even turned my hand, or should that be legs, to bike rides in the country. All to no avail.

I saw an advert for speed dating in Leicester Square this one hot summer night and decided I had nothing to lose. Other than a clock load of three minutes.

I came to the conclusion that even I couldn't go wrong with speed dating. Only three minutes with each man. Surely even I couldn't show myself up in that time frame.

This will come as no surprise to my friends or family, but I had a Savvy B to calm my nerves and give me a drop of Dutch courage. A rather large drop of Dutch courage. I say a glass, it was actually a bottle.

The bell rang and it was time for my first three-minute date. I was at a table with a rather handsome man, who at a guess, I would place in his early forties. He had such beautiful eyes, I felt myself start to swoon. I believed I was about to meet my perfect man.

Well, let me tell you this, whoever coined the phrase, looks can be deceiving deserves a medal. He opened his mouth to tell me his name was Derek. He had a voice which only the word monotone would be appropriate to describe. Trainspotter springs to mind.

After his first question, "Which is your favourite train model?" (I kid you not), we sat in silence. I don't think he was impressed with my answer. I told him my favourite train was Thomas. I mean, I was only joking but he had obviously had a sense of humour bypass. Before the bell rang to signal the end of the three minutes, he had already got up and left the date. RUDE. Things can only get better. I hoped.

I'd never been so grateful to hear a bell in my life. Well, apart from the dinner bell back in primary school. I was a fat kid, what can I say? I got up and moved to my next victim. Whoops, I mean my next date.

I found myself sat opposite another handsome man. But I told myself not to judge a book by its cover after my first failure. Wait until you hear him speak, I heard a voice in my head tell me. And when he did, I fell in love. He was very posh, well-spoken and far from monotone.

He asked me a question about my occupation and as my gob opened, I saw an eyebrow raise on his boat race. Our voices and accents couldn't be any more opposite. He clearly came from Barnes and me from Staines.

"It's like being on a date with a character from EastEnders!" I kid you not, those were the exact words that left his mouth. I would have raised my eyebrows too, but after Botox, I struggle to perform this action.

He was clearly put off by the way I spoke so instead of raising my eyebrows, I raised my arse from the seat and finished the date prematurely. Third time lucky I hoped as the bell rang again.

I clutched onto my glass of Savvy B and decided it WOULD be third time lucky. I may be the unluckiest gay in the dating world but I would never lose my optimism. PMA. Positive mental attitude. I'm going to have it etched on my gravestone.

I sat down at the next table, well, I use the word sat loosely. I'd had a few glasses of New Zealand plonk by this point, so the word stumble is a more appropriate description of how I travelled to my seat. I soon sobered up as I clapped eyes on my next potential beau. DING FUCKING DONG.

It was a refreshing joy to finally meet a VERY handsome man who seemed reasonably normal. And we seemed to hit it off like a house on fire. We laughed together and he even asked me out for a drink after the speed dating had finished. Maybe the undateable gay's curse was finally lifting....

Chapter Seventeen

My double date with lesbians (July 2005)

Well After my speed dating success, I was floating on the clouds. I couldn't believe it was third time lucky with my date. I was so excited about him. Let me introduce you to him.

His name was Paul, a 24-year-old funeral director from Windsor. Such a handsome chap with bright blue eyes. Oh my days, those eyes. Excuse the cheesy analogy but I could have gone swimming in his old pork pies.

I must confess, I was a little concerned by his chosen vocation. I've always imagined funeral directors to be big burly blokes who look like they could be extras in the *Terminator* films. And I've always pictured them to be rather dull and a possible necrophile.

I can see me getting lynched in the street now by a mob of Co-Operative funeral care workers. Please excuse my judgemental attitude. I must constantly remind myself of my Christian upbringing. My Sunday school teachers clearly made no impact on me.

Now for some reason, I was feeling rather nervous of a second date with Paul. I felt a fluttering of butterflies deep in my gut. For once, I was imagining that I might have actually met a man who may be around longer than just for a cup of coffee, the morning after. I wanted to make a good impression.

My dear friend Natalie, a lesbian, suggested that we make up a foursome with her then-girlfriend, Britney. No, not Britney Spears but she did have the similarity in that she was also American. But that's where the similarities ended.

We opted for a lovely little Italian restaurant in Windsor, the name of which escapes me. My memory is not what it once was.

After all the pleasantries were out of the way, we sat down and the conversation flowed like the Thames at high tide. I could see Paul had a glisten in his eye whenever we looked at each other. Well, I hope that's what it was and not the reflection of the candle in his pupil. The somersaults my stomach was doing would have been worthy of a gold medal in the Olympics.

As the waiter came to take our order, Paul suggested we share a garlic bread as a starter. Anyone who knows me well, will know I do NOT share food. Under any circumstance.

The mere suggestion of sharing a garlic bread made my eyebrows raise. Yes, they actually raised. I was still a week away from my Botox top-up appointment at the time.

Natalie, knowing my sheer greed, gaged my reaction and kicked me under the table. And gave me one of her death stares. She's a teacher so she has this look perfected. I gulped and begrudgingly agreed to share a starter. You may be sat there reading this, calling me a fat bastard. But I love my food and I want it all to myself. Maybe this is another thing I'm doing wrong that's contributing to my undateable status.

A few more Italian Pinots later and Natalie started interrogating my poor date.

"Would you like children one day? Because Mark would."

I nearly dropped my glass of Pinot. Of course, being such an alcoholic, I managed to grip it tight enough to ensure that didn't happen. Bit forward for a second date question, I thought to myself but at least it wasn't me who posed the question.

"I already have children." Paul immediately replied.

Just at that precise moment, I was taking a gulp of Pinot, and to say I spat it out and nearly choked on it would not be a dramatization.

"You've got children? Plural?" I asked.

"Yes", he seemed perfectly happy to talk about it and I did my best to pretend the subject hadn't shocked me.

"Oh my God. Boy or girl?" I asked, genuinely intrigued. I'd never met a gay man with a child.

"I have three sons."

Well, you could have heard a pin drop in that restaurant. No one said a word.

As my dear mum always tells her friends, I've never been speechless since the day she sent me to speech therapy when I was four. But I was certainly speechless now.

Whilst we're on the subject of my mum sending me to speech therapy. Yes, I understand people may find it hard to believe but I hadn't actually started talking, and being as though I was four years old, she started to worry. Hence why she marched me to speech therapy. But ever since that day, my mum always says she regrets sending me.

But I'm going off topic as usual. Back to the bombshell that had just been dropped in the Italian restaurant. As my friends will tell you, I don't handle myself in the best manner during serious situations. I have what you might call a nervous laugh. And God strike me down, this is how I reacted to this situation.

Natalie, having a tad more decorum than me, kicked me under the table again to indicate this was not an appropriate moment to activate my nervous laugh. As if I have control over it...

"Why are you kicking me?" I barked at Natalie, not immediately clocking on to why she had booted me with her size 5 Doc Martens.

Finally processing the information, I could see this was a brave bit of information to reveal so early on in our dating period. I grabbed his hand.

I could tell we both meant something to each other because he said he had never revealed this information to a potential boyfriend before. And so, I leant over and kissed him on the lips. I'm not one for PDA'S but this just felt the right moment.

"I hope I get to see you again after tonight", he said.

"Try and stop me." I replied.

Chapter Eighteen

Premature Ejaculations (August 2005)

I'd already been on two dates with my lovely blokey from my speed dating success story. And we'd just had our third. I kept thinking that any moment, someone was going to slap me and wake me up from my dream. I mean, not that I've got a fetish for being slapped or anything.

Three dates done and dusted: That's some kind of record for this gay boy, this undateable gay. I was expecting a knock on my door from The Guinness Book of Records any minute.

I decided that this was the right time to introduce him to my mother. So I arranged an afternoon tea with plenty of cakes. People who know me well will know that my biggest weakness, besides men, is cakes. Give me a Belgian bun and I'm like a pig in shit. Happy for hours.

KNOCK, KNOCK. That was us knocking on the door, by the way, arriving at my mum and dad's house. They actually have a doorbell so I don't know why I wrote knock, knock. It should have been DING DONG. Digressing.... anyway, you get the gist, we had arrived for afternoon tea.

As my mother answered the door, I could see her eyes light up at how handsome Paul was. She was acting like a bloody magpie seeing a glitter ball. You could see the pride in her eyes that her gay son had bagged himself a bit of a fitty. Although now I come to think about it, I don't like quite how shocked she seemed to be at me managing to bag myself such a handsome man. I must talk to her about that at a later date. Note to self.

I made the necessary introductions and Paul took my mother's hand and kissed it.

"Nice to meet you!"

Now for anyone who knows my mother, will know that she fills up and cries at the drop of a hat. The slightest thing makes her well up.

I've witnessed my mum cry at X Factor, Loose Women and even Homes under the Hammer. And this is exactly what I witnessed now. Obviously, Paul's good manners were too much for her and she felt overwhelmed. My god, I didn't know where to look. Although I was looking around for a hanky.

Once she'd pulled herself together and I'd given her a slap to stop her crying. (That's a joke, no need for the police. I don't actually beat my mother.) She finally poured the coffee and offered around her freshly made cherry macaroons.

My mummy is a bit of a Mary Berry when it comes to baking. She's always got tins upon tins of cakes ready for visitors.

Paul made a very good impression that afternoon and I could definitely tell that my mum approved. In fact, I'd known she'd approved from the moment she broke down in tears after the kiss on the hand.

As we left and walked to the car, I turned and gave Paul a kiss of my own. I planted a great big smacker on his lips.

"What was that for?" He gushed.

MASSIVE GREAT BIG STRENGTH SIX MATURE CHEDDAR CHEESE ALERT

"Just for being you," I replied.

Now, this next part may make some people call me a slut. What they call a slut, I call enjoying the male species. I think it's very important to try a few different platters from the buffet table, else how do you know what you like?

Anyway, I digress once again. The point I was getting to was that, here we were, three dates in and we still hadn't enjoyed any kind of sexual relations. (No Bill Clinton jokes here please).

So, to solve this dilemma, I asked him back to mine and before you could say blow job, I had him on my bed and we were enjoying a very passionate kiss. Fully clothed, may I add.

As I went to undo his trousers to rip them off, he grabbed my hand to stop me. I looked up, shocked, like a rabbit in headlights.

"Before you go there, there's something I need to tell you."

Well, talk about mind racing into overdrive moment. My mind filled with all sorts of visions and scenarios. After a silence of what felt like days, I pleaded.

"What? What is it Paul?"

"I've got a really small willy."

Phew. My mind slowed down and stopped racing. I looked up to the sky, thankful I wasn't about to unzip a pair of trousers and reveal a vagina. A small willy I can cope with. A vagina, I cannot.

Now, people who know me very well, will realise a small willy will never put me off. One, because I'm not a shallow, size Queen. And two, the good Lord did not bless me downstairs either.

In fact, a man once told me that he could use my penis as dental floss. (Bastard). But that's another story for another chapter.

To prove to Paul that the small willy revelation had not killed the passion, I continued in my quest and unzipped his trousers. And as I did, I got the almightiest surprise.

An eyeful of cum. As I blinked to remove the foreign object from my eye, his face turned a beautiful shade of Lobster.

"You just turn me on so much."

My one eye, the one not sealed shut with his natural adhesive, widened.

"Clearly. I mean, I know I'm good", I gushed, "but I'd hardly even touched you yet."

"I LOVE YOU!" He suddenly blurted out.

I sat back on the bed, still temporarily blinded in one eye.

"You what?" I was aghast.

"How can you love me? You barely know me."

"I can't help the way I've fallen for you."

Call me mental. Call me mad. Call me destined to be undate-able for a whole lifetime. But I just couldn't truly believe that someone could fall in love that quickly. And genuinely mean it. So I asked him to leave. And I never saw him again.

Chapter Nineteen

The Headlock (September 2006)

I was finally getting out of Budgens, heading off for pastures new at university. Yes, I was going off to do a degree. So I handed in my resignation and prepared myself for my final few weeks.

I also remember the moment I told Lynne that I was leaving her behind after five years together, gallivanting around the checkouts.

"I'm leaving."

After the initial silence, and then smacking me over the head with a French stick (I feel sorry for whoever bought that), she broke down in tears and wrapped her arms around me.

Never one for tears myself, I patted her on the back, rather condescendingly.

"There, there."

Finally prising her away from my body and attempting to dry off my wet chest from her tears, Serena, a new girl, came bowling up to us. She was a bit odd. And that's an understatement.

"Mark. My girlfriend has got a man she'd love to set you up with."

Alarm bells should have started ringing. But as any self-respecting gay man will tell you; you should never turn down any male opportunity that is presented to you.

"I've given him your number. I showed him a picture and he's still keen, even after seeing it. I didn't know if you'd be attractive enough for him."

BITCH, I thought.

"Do you think it's a good idea to have anything to do with a man Serena knows?" Lynne tried to advise me.

Anyway, ignoring Lynne and putting my fist in her gob to stop her in her quest of putting me off, I phoned John. That was his name, by the way.

RING RING.

"Hello?"

"Hello. Is that John?"

"Yes. Who's that?"

"I'm Mark. Serena gave me your number."

"Oh yes. She told me you might ring."

"Well. Shall we meet for a date?"

"Sure. Can you do tonight?"

"Cor, he's keen", I mouthed to Lynne.

"No problem", back to John, "Where shall we meet?"

"Shall we meet outside Butlins?" He suggested.

I suddenly thought I'd been propelled into a parallel universe.

"Butlins?!"

"Yeah. On the beach front in Bognor."

"You live in Bognor?"

Serena had failed to inform me of that little titbit of information. Well, in for a penny, in for a pound, I agreed in my head that I didn't have anything to lose. Besides a tank of petrol.

Driving down the A3 towards the south coast, I was blaring Rihanna's debut single, 'Pon de Replay' on repeat. Yes, I have an annoying habit of playing my favourite songs far too many times.

I arrived in Bognor and as quick as I drove up to the promenade, I wanted to turn the car around and drive just as quickly back to London. Without sounding like a snob, I felt like I'd just been dumped on a rough council estate, next to a beach.

But always one for seeing things through, I parked up and double, no triple, checked I had locked all the doors.

Seeing John for the first time, my jaw hit the pebbles. He was gorgeous with a capital G. We took a romantic stroll along the beach front and as the sun set on the god-awful back drop, John leant in for a snog. And I ended up staying the night.

Leaving John the next morning, we promised we'd see each other again. Driving back to London, I had love bubbles gurgling in my stomach. And I had, you guessed it, 'Pon de Replay' on repeat. Whenever I hear that song, even to this day, I think of John and how happy we could have been. That is if Serena hadn't interfered with her wooden spoon.

As I was price checking a packet of six toilet rolls for Lynne, I felt my mobile phone vibrate in my pocket. It was him.

"Hello John. I had such a great time last night."

"Well, it was the first and will be the last."

Confused, I dumped the bog rolls on the shelf and ran outside to get some nicotine.

"What are you talking about? What's changed since this morning?"

"Serena's told me what you've been doing to her. Bullying in the workplace is no joke. I won't be seeing you again."

And with that, the line went dead. The bastard had hung up on me. Steam erupting from my lug holes, I stomped my foot down on my Marlboro light and marched in to confront Serena.

Seeing her filling up the BWS, that's beers, wines and spirits for those who've never worked in a supermarket, I stormed up to her.

"Why did you tell John I was bullying you?"

"My girlfriend dumped me this morning. So I didn't think it fair if you started seeing her best mate."

I was gobsmacked. And she just laughed in my face. Expecting Jeremy Beadle to pop up around the corner any minute, I was sure this must be a wind up.

"You're lucky I'm leaving", I growled. "Just stay out of my way."

I went to push past her but at that moment, she put her foot out and tripped me up. I went down like a sack of shit, landing on a box full of sauvignon blanc.

"That's New Zealand wine", I screamed, "I hope for your sake none of that has smashed!"

And then the biggest shock of my life happened. Serena bent over and got me in a headlock. And she was doing a weird, hysterical laugh, like some psycho out of Prisoner: Cell Block H. I could feel my airways starting to block. Just as I started coughing and spluttering, trying my best to push her off, Lynne became the hero of the hour.

I'd never seen the Welsh windbag move so fast in all our years of working side by side. If only she'd been that quick at getting the customers through the tills, we might not have always had queues. But analysing staff efficiency wasn't really a priority right that minute.

Lynne came rushing up and pushed Serena away from my jugular.

"He deserved it", Serena spat and she walked out the store, never to be seen again. We never quite worked out why she had it in for me but I was just grateful for Lynne's new found speed.

66

"We need a drink!" I declared as I walked out of Budgens's doors for the last time.

"To the Crossroads!" Lynne screamed.

Realising I wouldn't be working with Lynne anymore, it was her turn to pat me on the back.

"There, there, my little poof."

I cried into my Savvy B. It was the end of an era. But thank God I'd not been choked to death and was still alive to see the next chapter of my life begin.

Chapter Twenty

The armpit muncher (February 2007)

J ust when I thought I might find a man who enjoyed a plain and simple sex life, along came Jude. Now Jude wasn't a fan of kissing on the lips very much. Oh no, he liked to rummage his face in my armpits and kiss those instead.

The day he text me and told me not to wear any deodorant that night was the day I feigned a migraine and never did he grace my armpits again.

Chapter Twenty-One

My accidental trip into prostitution (May 2007)

I was just nearing the end of my first year at university. But bugger me gently, did I underestimate the cost of gaining your degree.

I was doing a few waiting on shifts at the local Harvester. With my gift of the gab, I used to make quite a few tips but it still wasn't enough. The only other perk of the job was salivating over the chavvy boys who used to come in to eat. And they would always be wearing grey jogging bottoms. I don't know what it is about a man in grey joggers but it don't half get my pulse racing and my juices flowing.

One night I was flicking through google on my laptop. "How to earn extra money" in my search engine. Up came all these get rich quick schemes. A load of old shit, until I finally saw one that caught my eye.

MOBILE MASSAGE THERAPISTS WANTED FOR AGENCY; the advertisement read. It would be perfect for me. I'd trained as a masseur back in my late teens and I'd been pretty damn good at it but never had the chance to do it as a job.

And this agency was offering £37 an hour. My eyes lit up. That was a lot of money back then. Especially for a student. And certainly more than I'd ever earnt an hour.

Before you could say, "How's that pressure sir?", I'd been placed on the books as a freelance therapist for this agency.

A week later and I'd been sent the details of my first client. A man called Brian and I was to call at his flat in Kings Cross.

I don't mind telling you, I was shitting a brick on my way. A stiff vodka on the tube soon calmed my nerves. Yes, you could still drink on the underground in those days without fear of the old bill giving you a fine.

As I got to the front door of this rather plush apartment block opposite St Pancras station, I nearly turned around and got back on the Piccadilly line.

But I reminded myself that it was thirty seven big ones and gave myself a good firm talking to.

I pressed the buzzer and as Brian opened the door, I didn't know where to avert my gaze.

He was standing there, stark bollock naked. I wasn't sure whether to cry for my mum or look up to the sky and thank the Lord. Especially as it was a rather large tool that was dangling between this Brian's legs.

"Come in!" His voice was incredibly butch and I noticed an American twang. So that explains the lack of foreskin, I thought to myself. Not that I'd been studying his manhood or anything.

I must confess, I'm awfully fond of foreskin, so seeing a penis circumcised is not my favourite thing. But a cock's a cock and it was still one worth looking at.

Brian oozed confidence out of every orifice and made me follow him into the bedroom. He lashed himself face down and out came my oil bottle. No, that's not a euphemism. Every good masseur must have a bottle of oil.

As I started effleurage on Brian's back, (that's a long sweeping massage stroke for those of you not in the know) I began to notice his bottom bobbing up and down on the bed. And the odd groan escaping from his lips.

As you all know, I was brought up a good Catholic boy so I'm not one to pass judgement. But my eyes did widen in their sockets. Being the professional I am though, I continued on with my effleurage.

As I got to his glutes, that's the posh terminology for arse, I saw his, not so little, man pop out from under his gouch to say hello.

He was erect. And I don't mind telling you, so was I.

He rolled over onto his back so I could continue with his massage and his penis nearly had my eye out. Popped up like a coiled spring, it did.

Brian looked at me.

Then looked down at his willy.

And then looked back at me.

Then glanced back down at his penis.

And then I fixed my eyes on his dick.

And before you could say, bend me over Betty, my mouth had accidentally wrapped itself around his manhood.

I performed my act of fellatio, to a very gratified audience, who grabbed at my hair. (YES, I still had hair to grab.) He let out moans in all the right places.

As I swallowed, well, it's rude to spit, Brian stood up and gave me £90.

Counting it, I said, "But the agency pay me."

"That's your tip", Brian told me as he showed me to the front door.

I made my way back to Kings Cross tube, tapping my pocket that the ninety quid was in. I had to phone Tullene.

"Tullene. I've just been paid £90 for a blow job!"

"You're a prostitute!" She retorted.

Chapter Twenty-Two

His First Chance (July 2007)

Michael. That name takes me back to my university days, way back in 2007. I've been undateable most of my adult life. If I carry on at this rate, I'll do a Bridget Jones and be found in my flat, all alone, eaten by Alsatians.

So, I'd been chatting away to this guy on Gaydar. God, I'm showing my age again. The days before Grindr entered the gay scene and took promiscuity to a whole new level. His name was Michael and after a fortnight of making small talk, I suggested we meet for a date. He came over all shy and told me he gets nervous of dates. I felt like giving his face a slap. Man up, I wanted to type, but I kept the words inside my head.

He told me his friends were throwing him a birthday bash in the Village, a small bar-cum-dance floor in Soho, for you non-gay readers. He invited me along. Alarm bells should have started ringing at this point, but being the hopeless romantic that I am, I thought, fuck it, I'll go! It should take the nerves out of the first date, I reasoned.

But, as I wouldn't know anyone, I decided I must take a friend. Cue my university partner in crime and best friend, Thwack. Not her real name but one I coined for her on the first day our eyes met in our history of English lecture.

Thwack was a little unsure at first but after a gentle arm twisting, literally, (she brings out my vicious side), I persuaded her. We decided to get on the night bus which takes you straight into Soho. That was an eventful bus ride, which still haunts us to this day.

We jumped on the 207 on a dark winter's night and opted to sit upstairs on the double decker beast. A decision we still regret. As we journeyed through Southall and then Ealing, we were joined on the upper deck by people who I will describe as undesirable. Think Jeremy Kyle participants and you'll be half way there. They were very loud and liked to swear. Now, don't get me wrong, I like to have a good swear as much as the next person, but they took swearing to a whole new level of Tourette's.

As they got louder and their Tourette's seemed to get uncontrollable, our eyes widened with fear. We didn't say a word. We didn't have to. We looked at each other and I just knew we were thinking the exact same thing. Were we going to make it to Soho alive? Nervous laughter soon kicked in which whipped us into even more of a frenzy. We were holding onto each other's hands for dear life, clammy palms into the bargain.

As I saw the bus pull into Tottenham Court Road, I jumped up from my seat quicker than a fat kid whose had McDonald's waved in front of his face. I felt like performing fellatio on the bus driver, to show my gratitude for surviving the bus ride alive.

We literally couldn't get off that 207 quick enough and before you could say drag queen, we were inside the Village, large vodkas in hand. Michael came to introduce himself. My god, he wasn't lying about being shy. It took him ten minutes to tell me his name. After a quick beverage, it loosened him up and we had a little dance, shared a little lingering kiss and then me and Thwack decided another vodka was in order. I kissed Michael and told him, I'll be back. Just call me Arnie!

Now, I'm not even joking you, we couldn't have been gone more than five minutes, but as we turned around, Michael was nowhere to be seen. For those of you who have frequented the Village, you'll know there's not many places to hide. We scoured the place, toilets, dance floor, smoking area. He had done a fucking Houdini on us and vanished...

Chapter Twenty-Three

His Second Chance (a day later in 2007)

S o, I remember laying in bed the morning after the night before.

In case your memory needs jogging from the last page, the night before was when Houdini, AKA Michael twat bag wank piece, vanished from sight on our first date. Ooh, if my mum is reading this, she will wash my mouth out with Fairy Liquid. Yes, she did used to do that when I was a child. But then I can't blame her, I have always had a mouth like a Sailor.

I rolled over and pulled open the curtains. Cor, the sun hit my eyes like a slap around the chops with a wet cod. And the realisation dawned on me that the previous night's date was not a dream. It was a harsh reality. What could have happened to him?

I suddenly became all drama queen. What if he was kidnapped? What if he's lying in the bottom of the Thames, with bricks tied to his feet? Before my imagination ran any more wilder than John Wayne's stallion, my phone beeped with a text message. My jaw slapped down on my blue pillowcase like a sack of potatoes. It was from Michael.

My first instinct was to lob my phone out of the window. But my calm, non-drama queen side kicked in and I decided to press open on the message instead. What a novel idea.

"I'm really sorry about last night. Everyone decided to move on to another club and we couldn't find you to tell you."

Mmm, my mind started ticking. It seemed a plausible excuse but then I thought, why didn't you just text me last night to tell me where you were?? I quickly text him my thought and he replied;

"I was just so drunk. I didn't think. Sorry again."

At least I knew he wasn't being held captive on some pirate ship or being used for fish food at the bottom of the Thames.

As I dragged myself from my pit, he text me again.

"Do you wanna do something tonight?"

My nostrils flared like George's dragon. The bare-faced cheek of the man. Actually, not man. Boy.

But then I suddenly thought to myself, I can't be a bitter old queen for the rest of my living days.

"I'm going to an aerobics class with my mate tonight. You're welcome to join."

He accepted. But how events unfolded later that day, it's a decision he came to regret.

Cue Tullene. Hell hath no fury like this girl when her gay best friend has been scorned by a boy.

I drove to Michael's house and he jumped in the front seat. He began by being very bashful but soon started talking and I decided I would let bygones be bygones. As we pulled up outside Tullene's house, I saw her walk towards the car abnormally and uncharacteristically fast. She's not really much for exercise is our Tullene. She threw a death glare at Michael. If looks could have killed, he'd have been ten foot under. I couldn't work out whether it was her protective nature or the fact that she had to sit in the back of the car.

The car journey to the leisure centre was rather frosty and, for a girl with a gob the size of the Grand Canyon, it was also very quiet. I broke the awkward silence.

"Tullene! This is Michael."

Her nostrils flared. And if you know Tullene, this is a very scary prospect and sight.

"So, you're Michael? That scrawny little runt who just upped and left Mark in a London club."

She barked worse than a Jack Russell.

As if the car ride wasn't awkward enough, I looked in the rear-view mirror and saw Tullene's ears doing an impersonation of a kettle.

Michael seemed lost for words which didn't help his case against Tullene. She hates to be ignored. I saw her arm reach for the seat belt and she went to tug on it. I gasped and shouted, "TULLENE!"

Phew! I saved the poor boy from seat belt strangulation.

In my capacity as peace maker, I manged to defuse the situation.

"I've given Michael a second chance. So I'd really love it if you did too. For me."

Her nostrils began to deflate to a normal size and I could see her starting to calm down. She also loosened her grip that she had on his seat belt.

As we drove towards the local leisure centre, Michael pulled the passenger mirror down and started admiring himself. I saw Tullene's nostril's flapping.

"No wonder men find me so attractive." He smiled at his reflection. I did not.

As we arrived at the aerobics class, I started to take a dislike to

Michael's personality. He was very cocky and he actually began to get on my moobs.

We managed to get through the aerobics class without talking and towards the end, he got a stitch. It couldn't have happened to a nicer person.

As we dabbed the sweat from our brows, I decided I couldn't bear to spend another minute in the presence of Michael. I felt like I might develop a rash just by breathing the same air as him. We all went to get in the car and I turned to Michael.

"There's only enough room for me and Tullene."

His jaw dropped. And so did hers.

"There's a bus stop over there!"

Tullene high fived my orange palm and we drove off, leaving Michael doing a very impressive impression of a fish. Now that's gay power.

Chapter Twenty-Four

When a date turns UGG-ly (November 2007)

S o, there I was. A few months after the Michael fiasco. In Soho, waiting at a fondue restaurant. My date this time was called Simon. He was a buyer for Mulberry. Mmm, now I'm no shallow man but this instantly excited me. I decided that he must have a rather decently sized.... bank account! Not that finances are an instant winner for me. But it does help. I can't have anyone wanting to feed from my bank account.

As he entered, I found he was rather pleasing on the eye. A bonus point in his favour. I know people say that looks aren't everything but I really couldn't imagine shagging someone who looks like the back end of the N7. All red and fumes squirting from every orifice. That is definitely no turn on for moi.

We sparked instantly. He talked of mulberry handbags. I have a rather sparse knowledge of Mulberry handbags. My friend is a manager for one of their stores at Heathrow. She hardly talks about the brand but I knew enough to engage in the conversation. This reminds me of a funny moment we once shared in Mexico. She was talking about handbags but mishearing, she thought we were taking the piss out of her. My manager friend turned her head and said, "I know my fucking materials!"

My mouth opened wide and dropped to my sun lounger, said "what?" Realising we weren't taking the piss; she continued her conversation. To this day, I have no recollection of why she thought we were being detrimental to her career. She was pissed, as she often is, and was put on PubWatch in our local town. Basically, this means that you are banned from entering any pub in the town. If I want to embarrass her, I threaten to bring up this story from our youth. It normally shuts her up. Oh, blackmail is a wonderful tool.

After realising that he failed to find this conversation amusing, I thought I should leave the restaurant. But my mother always taught me, "if you start something, you must see it through." I could hear her London accent echo through my ears. She was my inspiration to carry on.

We shared a cheese fondue. It was all sticky and gooey. We were dipping bread sticks in like it was a euphemism for what was to come later. And at this point, I really did think the euphemism would come to fruition. We finished our main and we had had a few belly laughs. Belly laughs? Surely that means a second date is on the cards. We ordered a dessert. If you stay for dessert, you are bound to be invited for coffee. And one hopes the coffee ain't going to be at the restaurant table.

Desert of chocolate fondue with marshmallows finished, I suggested we frequent G-A-Y Late for a cocktail and a dance. Praying it's not an I, he accepted. As we entered the bar, he went up and ordered me a sex on the beach. Yes, I admit, that is my cocktail of choice. Yes, I admit, I am a slut and hoped this would engage my date's brain to adopt this thought process. Unlucky for me, it failed and he didn't decide to whisk me off to Brighton beach for a quickie.

As I got over the fact he wasn't going to whisk me off to the beach, I remembered that I had just purchased a brand new pair of UGG boots! Please don't ask me why I was wearing UGG boots on a date. I have no idea to this day.

Excited to show off my new purchase, I cocked my leg up. Well, the bastard didn't believe that they were real. At his disbelief, I cocked my leg higher to show off the UGG logo. I think I'd had one too many sexes on the beach because I lost my balance. My hand landed directly in his genitalia region. If it wasn't for my fake tan, you would've been able to see my red-faced embarrassment. I apologised profusely but the frigid knob thought it was a come on.

"That's a bit forward!" He proclaimed.

"It was an accident." I protested.

He got up and walked out of G-A-Y Late. Yes, left me all on my tod. He obviously wasn't the man for me. Was any man ever going to be? That was the thought I was left with as I stood there, empty cocktail glass in hand, real Ugg boots on feet.

Chapter Twenty-Five

Once Is Enough – Apparently... (December 2007)

I didn't let Michael or Simon deter my quest of true love. Back in the saddle, there I was in a gay club, dancing the night away in my best new loafers. I had a wine in my right hand but no man in my left. Someone get the violins out. It was a Saturday night and the only love in my life was Sauvignon Blanc from the Marlborough estate. But as if Paul Daniel's just waved his magic wand, a potential date was suddenly upon me like a fly on shit.

The music was loud and, as my friends will inform you, my hearing is not the best. Many a time I have the television on so loud, the neighbours from two doors down bang away on my front door. Anyway, I struggled to hear this potential beau's name but my inhibitions had been lost in a bottle of Oyster Bay. So I went straight in for a kiss.

And in the profound words of Cher, it really is in his kiss. Instantly I felt a connection and I swooned. Maybe my long line of frog kissing is finally over, I excitedly decided. From that moment on, we spent the entire evening locked lipped and it reiterated my feelings that no more amphibians may cross my luscious lips.

The end of the evening drew near and I sensed mini me getting a little aroused. He thought he's going to be getting some action from this nameless man. My future beau walked to his taxi and I presumptuously attempted to join him inside the taxi. But to mine and mini me's dismay, he put his hand up to signal no entry. Instead, he slipped me his phone number on a piece of paper. Not what I'd hoped he'd be slipping me that night.

I woke up with a start the next day and quickly rolled over, anticipating a Sunday morning session. My hopes were instantly dashed when my memory kicked in and I remembered I ended up in bed alone. I picked my phone up, hazy eyed. I had a text from an unknown number, from a bloke called Simon. Oh my god, so that was his name! The stark realisation hit me that my last attempt at romance was with that tosser from Mulberry. Also called Simon. Not a good omen but I reminded myself of my religious upbringing and I promised not to judge a man by his name.

We arranged a date for the following night and he suggested a restaurant in Uxbridge, close to where he lives. Judgmental Mark kicked in and I decided he doesn't have a lot going for him. One, his name was Simon and two, he lives in Uxbridge. But again, I will not sit in judgment.

The following evening arrived and I found myself with sweaty palms and shallow breathing to deal with. I didn't know what I was more nervous about, being in Uxbridge town centre or going on a date. And then something hit me like a wet fish around my boat race. I didn't have a clue what Simon looked like as I was so intoxicated, that that part of my memory seems to have been erased by Sauvignon.

I had my fingers crossed he wasn't a dog. I walked in and spotted a figure standing and waving in my direction. I'm no intellectual giant but I concluded that must be him. He wasn't bad on the eye. I wouldn't have kicked him out of bed.

The conversation flowed between us but unfortunately for my date, so did the Sauvignon Blanc. As each glass glided down my oesophagus, my voice raised a decibel. We laughed, we talked, we ate. I really thought it had gone well. My future prince was sat in front of me. Frogs were to become a distant memory. Boy, was I delusional! As I asked, "when shall we see each other next?", he replied deadpan, "once was enough!"

Open mouthed, I got deserted by him at the table. Note to self, avoid Simons.

Chapter Twenty-Six

The foot fetish (April 2008)

T hen there was Neil. He was a Scottish man so that should have sent alarm bells ringing immediately.

He arrived one night on my doorstep, carrying a bottle of Scotch. How romantic to be bearing gifts, I thought. Especially Scotch. I'm rather partial to a wee dram, truth be told.

After a wee dram or three, he started to kiss me. On the lips. RESULT. No armpits. I laid back and breathed a sigh of relief to be finally getting the plain and simple sex life I'd been craving.

"Let me suck you!" He demanded.

Who was I to say no? As he continued to kiss his way down my body, he got to my flies. Mini Mark was poised and ready for action.

But as I looked down, I found him at my knees. Maybe the scotch had clouded his judgment and as I tried to re-direct his head back up, his lips continued on their journey south.

Before I could say Loch Lomond, I felt my sock being ripped from my foot.

And before I could say Reflexology, he was sucking my big toe.

Chapter Twenty-Seven

I don't FORE-SKIN a future with him... (June 2008)

I'm telling this tale at the risk of being called a shallow, vain, poof. I'm even scared that people may start hurling rotten potatoes at me in the street. But oh well, I have been called a gay Joan Rivers many a time so I'll take the risk.

I'm hard as nails. Normally in a gay sauna, I am. Anyway, I'm digressing. I like to think I am, but underneath my fake tanned, Botox-ed hard-hearted exterior, I'm a pussy cat.

As my friends will tell you, I don't really have a type when it comes to men. My criteria normally just states they must have a cock and a pulse. And sometimes even the pulse isn't important. No, no, I'm joking, I'm joking. I thought I'd better point that out before I get arrested by the Old Bill for necrophilia. The point is, I'm very open minded when it comes to men, hence why I don't have a type. There is just one strict criterion my men must adhere to. GOOD TEETH.

I can't bear bad teeth. It turns my stomach. The thought that I have to kiss them if their gnashers aren't up to scratch. Now, I'm not talking wonky wisdoms. That I can cope with, it's just when they're discoloured and stained. I just think, get yourself down the hygienist.

Now before you all start lynching me and throwing stones in my direction, let me point me out that I'm not perfect. I have a little gap in my front teeth. But I gargle coconut oil every night to ensure they stay gleaming white. People have to put sunglasses on when I smile.

Talking of my gap, it takes me back to a family roast one Sunday. We'd finished eating and my mum looked at me and said, "you've got something in your teeth!"

So there I was having a little pick to remove the foreign object. I looked back at my mother, waiting for reassurance it was gone. "No, no. It's still there!" So I picked again. And again. This went on for a full five minutes so I stood up from the table in sheer frustration and walked to the mirror. On further investigation, I realised it was my gap she was referring to and there was absolutely nothing there!

"30 years you've known me and you thought it was food stuck and not my gap!"

I'd been set up on a date by my friend Lucy Inch again. You know the one who works for Mulberry. I thought I'd give her another chance to get it right. Surely, she'd do better this time. So, off I trotted to the restaurant to meet this lovely bloke called Lee. He looked very handsome as he stood up at the dinner table to greet me with a kiss. What manners.

We sat down and I ordered the standard bottle of Sauvignon from New Zealand. My snobby ways never cease to amaze me. The waiter pours it for us and as we lift our glasses to cheers, he shot me a bloody great smile.

How sweet.

Then my jaw dropped quicker than a prostitute's knickers.

His smile included some rather discoloured teeth. I knocked back my glass of Sauvignon like an alcoholic at breakfast.

He's so handsome, I kept repeating to myself. And then he'd open his mouth and it reminded me of my bad teeth phobia. I did spend hours on Google looking for the official name for it, but there isn't one. Even though there is an ARACHIBUTYRO-PHOBIA which is the fear of peanut butter sticking to the roof of your mouth, I kid you not. (??!!)

Lee and I, we did get on really really well, and we laughed and we enjoyed a beautiful meal together. He had the looks and the personality. I tried to remember my Sunday school teaching and vowed to overcome my shallow behaviour when it came to his molars. We got up to leave and he went to kiss me. I pulled away, faster than a rat up a drainpipe.

I wasn't quite ready for that.

I made my excuses about bad breath from the food and he asked me back to his. I shocked myself and said yes. I told myself, I can't bring myself to kiss him on the lips but maybe I can kiss his...

Black taxi hailed (Yes, Uber hadn't been born yet), we arrived back at his gaff and to avoid another attempt from Lee at a kiss on the lips, I automatically dropped to my knees.

As I performed fellatio, I heard his screams. I carried on, gloating and smiling to myself. He was obviously enjoying it. I felt quite smug as I continued.

He screamed again and I thought, God, I'm better at blow jobs than I thought I was. As he let out another scream, I decided, ooh I better just check he's alright.

I pulled away and I felt his foreskin come with me! I realised it was caught in my gap!

"Be careful!" He screamed as he rubbed himself better.

"Oh sorry!" I blushed. "It's my gap!"

Chapter Twenty-Eight

My time in a Turkish bath (August 2008)

After nearly circumcising Lee with my gap, Tullene and I decided it was time for a holiday. Before you could say, "Wish you were here", we were boarding a plane at Heathrow.

Has anyone ever been to Turkey? If you haven't, I really recommend that you do. The weather is beautiful, the resorts are luscious and the men are tall, dark and handsome.

The only annoying thing about Turkey is that you can't walk more than a hundred yards down the road without someone trying to sell you something. Whether it be a boat trip, apple tea or a fake football shirt.

But the one thing I didn't mind getting stopped and sold in the street was the offer of a Turkish bath. When you have a tall, dark, handsome man offering you a foam rub down and an oil massage, any proper gay man answers yes.

The next thing we knew, we were inside the Turkish bath and were very excited. We got ourselves dressed appropriately,

Tullene in a swimsuit, me in a pair of Speedos. And we got taken down for part one of the Turkish bath.

We were laid out on a round, marble slab. And they began washing us from head to toe in this delightful foam. Ooh, I tell you, I felt like a gay Marilyn Munroe in that iconic bath photo shoot.

After we'd had buckets of hot water lashed over us to wash off the foam, we were moved onto part two of our spa experience. The sea salt exfoliation massage.

I couldn't wait to have all my dead skin cells scrubbed away. As any fake tan addict will tell you, a full body exfoliation is just what one needs every now and again to avoid crusty elbows and knees.

But the men doing the scrub were rather rough. I felt like I was being exfoliated by Hulk Hogan. I started screaming because it felt like they were ripping the skin fresh from my calves.

Now, before I tell you the next part of the experience, I must make you aware of Tullene's nickname. We all call her T-bag. Probably something to do with her name beginning with T and the fact she's an old bag.

So, whilst I was having the skin ripped from my calves, I started shouting "T-bag! T-bag!", to convey to Tullene I was in pain.

But the Scottish boys, who were on the marble slab with us, obviously didn't know this was Tullene's nickname. I suddenly heard Scottish accents shouting,

"He wants them to T-bag him!"

Oh, the cringe-worthy embarrassment.

After surviving the skin peeling calf exfoliation and the Scottish T-bagging, we were swiftly moved onto our oil massage. As we walked along, I saw one of the male therapists winking at me.

Well, I think he was winking at me. That or he had a nervous twitch. I couldn't work out which one.

The male therapist suddenly stopped and grabbed me by the shoulder. He whispered in my ear in his seductive Turkish accent, "you're beautiful!"

Well, I blushed. Although you probably couldn't tell as the 46-degree Turkish heat had sunburnt my face.

As we carried on walking, something took me completely by surprise. I suddenly felt a finger slip up my ring piece, along with some material from my speedos. Well, my eyes nearly popped out of their sockets. How forward. Not that I was complaining.

He took us into our very own beauty room, which had two Massage beds waiting for us.

"Lay on the beds! Face down!" He barked.

We did as we were told but Tullene looked up. He obviously wasn't happy at her disobedience.

"FACE DOWN!" He barked again at Tullene.

We both started doing our nervous laughs that we're famous for. And then I felt another tap on my shoulder. As I looked up, I was greeted by a rather large Turkish erection. It practically took my eye out.

But it seemed such a shame to waste a perfectly good erection. So we swiftly asked Tullene to leave the room.

Chapter Twenty-Nine

My Turkish Barman (The same week in August 2008)

After being molested at the Turkish bath, (not that I was complaining mind you) Tullene and I decided that we needed a stiff drink.

Back at our hotel, I headed up to the bar to order us both a Sex on the Beach. Now, Pina colada is usually my cocktail of choice. But after my rather intimate massage that afternoon, I decided I'd had enough of creamy concoctions for one day.

As I browsed the cocktail menu; Actually, I don't know why I was browsing the menu. We'd already set our hearts on a Sex on the Beach but it was just something to occupy my hands as I waited for service.

And boy, was it worth the wait.

"What can I get for you?" I heard a sexy accent purr.

I looked up and I felt as though the next few moments passed by in slow motion. My eyes were greeted by the most handsome man I think I'd ever seen. Olive skin, hazel eyes and the most dazzling black hair. I licked my lips and had forgotten to answer the barman to give him our order.

"Sir?"

Giving myself a metaphorical slap, I shook myself out of my slow-motion love gaze. I shot him the most sexy smile my lips could muster.

"Two Sex on the Beach please."

"You a Londoner?"

I nodded. He returned my smile with an equally gorgeous one of his own.

"I love your accent", he told me.

"I love your accent." I reciprocated his compliment.

"My name is Ahmet."

AHMET. I swooned and imagined how that name would sound as I shouted it in the midst of passion.

"My name is Mark."

Handing me the cocktails, he winked as I walked off.

"See you soon, I hope." I'll make sure of it, I said in my head.

"I've just met the man I'm going to marry", I informed Tullene as I handed her our afternoon tipples.

"I thought I was going to die of fucking thirst." Nice, I thought, don't you worry about me having just met my future husband.

Now, no holiday to Turkey would be complete without a jeep safari, which is what we did to entertain ourselves the next day.

Our jeep picked us up from our hotel and off we went out into the wild, in convoy with other holiday makers. As we drove up into the mountains, our driver handed us water guns. Bemused, me and Tullene looked at each other.

"You have water fight with other jeeps!"

I saw Tullene turn a rather peculiar pale shade as she touched her wig. Now, Tullene is very protective over her array of wigs and it would take a very brave man to ever put water anywhere near her bonce. As it turned out, there were many brave men around that day and she had to accept the fate of that particular hair piece.

Drenched and looking like drowned rats, we were taken to the final stop on our safari. To this day, I still haven't worked out why it was called a safari. For, we saw no animals, just lots of mountains and water.

We arrived at the famous Marmaris wishing tree. I don't think it can be that famous because we had never heard of it. But legend has it, you have to make a wish whilst stroking the trunk. So, we did as we were told.

I know as a general rule of thumb you're meant to make a wish in your head but I couldn't resist saying mine out loud as I touched the bark.

"Please let me marry Ahmet!"

Desperate to get back to our accommodation to see if this infamous tree would live up to its reputation, our driver started off on our journey back down the mountains.

To say his driving was erratic would be an understatement. He was driving so close to the edge of this cliff, that we feared our lives were nearing their ends. Tullene grabbed my hand and our nervous laughs sparked.

Mistaking our nervous laughter for enjoyment, our chauffeur decided he would head even closer to the edge. So close in fact, that I'm not entirely convinced all four tyres were actually making contact with the road.

As we pulled up outside our all-inclusive establishment, I'd never seen Tullene move so fast as she darted from the jeep, white as a sheep.

Having recovered from our near-death experience, we dressed for dinner. As it was our last night, I made a particular effort being as though it was my last chance to impress Ahmet and bag my Turkish delight.

It turned out my efforts were well appreciated. Making my way to the bar, I noticed Ahmet smile and saw a twinkle sparkle in his hazel iris.

"You look so handsome tonight."

I nearly fainted as I heard the words leave his gob.

"He told me I look so handsome tonight", I beamed as me and Tullene sat down for dinner.

"Then bloody ask him out. We go home tomorrow."

But I couldn't. I felt so shy.

"But I will write to him when we get home."

Bags packed, we sat down for our final breakfast the next morning. Feeling deflated that we would be leaving Turkey and my future husband behind, I comfort ate and shovelled toast into my mouth like it was the last supper. And then I felt it get stuck.

Coughing and spluttering, I managed to spit out the words.

"Tullene. I think I'm choking."

Cue Tullene's nervous laugh. Instead of calling for help. Great, I was about to die in Turkey with a holiday companion whose about as good in an emergency as my three-year-old nephew.

Standing up to try and dislodge the piece of toast, Ahmet dashed over to our table and wrapped his arms around my ribcage. I felt his muscular physique push up against my back. But this scenario was not quite how I'd imagined our first time of being so intimate would pan out.

Thrusting me from behind, I saw the throat blocking object fly from my mouth and hit Tullene smack bang in the middle of her forehead. Now, who says there's no Karma?

Relieved I was alive to live another day, I grabbed Ahmet's hand.

"Thank you for saving my life."

"It was my pleasure."

"We're going home this morning."

Awkward silence invoked as I waited for him to declare his undying love and beg me not to fly back to London. But no.

"Goodbye Mark. I hope to see you again one day."

And he was gone.

As our plane took off from Dalaman airport, I stared down at the distant landscape, tear in my eye as I left Ahmet behind.

Landing at Heathrow, still having not forgiven Tullene for nearly letting me die on a piece of toasted Hovis, we walked towards baggage reclaim in silence.

Until I noticed a face from the past, obviously awaiting his own luggage. Nudging Tullene rather dramatically, I whispered,

"Tullene."

"Oh. Talking to me now?" She's stubborn, she is.

"Don't look now..."

Why do we always say that people? You know immediately that whomever you're talking to is likely to feast a look. I tried to drag us away but it was too late. He'd seen us and gave us a wave. There was no time to pretend we hadn't seen him and I forced my best smile as he made his way towards us.

"What am I going to say to him? I haven't seen him since I bashed into his trolley in Budgens."

"Ask him why he never called", Tullene bitterly suggested.

There was no time left to debate what my first words to him were going to be. Travis was standing right in front of us.

"Travis. What a tan." It was the best I could manage.

"Nice to see you both", he said, leaning over to kiss our cheeks.

"Is it?" Tullene blurted out. Shooting her my best daggers, she decided not to pursue that path of conversation.

"Been on holiday?" It was the only question that my brain could muster right then.

"No. I just thought I'd hang out around baggage reclaim to get inspiration for a suitcase for my next holiday." Well, Travis had obviously taken a college course in sarcasm. Feigning laughter and sticking my fist in Tullene's gob so she couldn't retaliate, I was lost for words. What I wanted to say was...

"Why didn't you phone me to take me on a date three years ago, you jumped up little prick?"

But what I actually said was...

"It would be lovely to meet up sometime."

Noticing Tullene's mouth was getting ready to blurt out a provocative statement, I accidentally, on purpose, stamped my size eight loafer down on her flip flop wearing feet. That made her think better of it.

"Oh yes, that would be lovely." Travis replied. "Have you still got the same number?"

"Yes. Anyway, I think I can see our luggage. Come on Tullene."

"I'll definitely call you!" Travis called after us as I dragged Tullene towards the belt.

Back home for a week, I still hadn't stopped dreaming of Ahmet. And, surprise, surprise, Travis hadn't called either.

Deciding I couldn't give up on a future with Ahmet, I wrote him a love letter.

Dear Ahmet,

It was so lovely to meet you when I was in Turkey. And thank you for saving my life. Here is my phone number. 07810432352. Please call me anytime. It would be lovely if you could come to visit me in London. I thought you were so gorgeous. I look forward to hearing from you.

All my love,

Mark xx

"But you don't know his surname or his address. How are you

going to send the letter?" Tullene brought me back down to earth with a bump.

I had a brainwave.

"I shall stick a photo of him on the envelope and send it to the hotel address."

So that's what I did. I marched down to Snappy Snaps and ordered the sales assistant to superimpose his picture onto the envelope.

I don't know if the letter got lost in the post or if Ahmet just wasn't interested, but I never received a reply.

Chapter Thirty

That time I attempted a detox (After Turkey in 2008)

N ow, I'm not talking a man/dating detox. Oh god, no. I couldn't do that. It'd be like depriving Dot Cotton of her cigarettes. No, I'm talking a lifestyle detox.

When I stepped on the scales after our indulgent holiday in Turkey, they spoke to me, "one at a time please!" For any of you less intellectually-minded people out there, the scales didn't actually talk. But you get the idea. I'm carrying quite a bit more weight around with me than a few months ago.

So I decided it was time to take action before I become any more undateable than I already appear to be. My lifestyle detox consisted of making sure I got eight hours sleep a night, protein shakes, a healthy meal a day, no alcohol (God help me) and definitely no cakes or crap! Wish me luck.

DAY ONE: I strongly advise anyone partaking in a protein shake diet to carry a packet of extra strong mints with you at all times. Oh my god. The breath. I could have woken the dead with my breath. The hardest part of my day was on my way home from work. I was filled with sheer excitement at the prospect of a glass of wine and The Bill. And then the reality of my detox hit me like a double decker bus. No wine! I could have cried. So, I got into bed with the hump. Oh well, at least that's my eight hours sorted.

DAY TWO: I decided I should go for a little swim today. I thought perving on the men in speedos might cheer me up and take my mind off my wine withdrawal. My god, I went dizzier than a fat chav whose been plonked smack bang in the middle of a circular McDonald's. Note to self; avoid exercise until the life-style detox is over.

DAY THREE: I feel an over share coming on. My stomach is more blown up than a balloon arch. I am more constipated than a person whose taken an overdose of Imodium. But on the plus side, I have been waking up with a much clearer head. It must be the enormous amount of sleep I'm getting and the lack of wine consumption.

DAY FOUR: It's only been three days, I know, but this morning, I decided to weigh myself. I was feeling that I surely must have shed a few pounds. As I stepped on, the scales told me I was exactly the same weight. Not a single bloody ounce had shed from my body. Oh well, I guess it was a bit soon to be expecting any weight loss. But it didn't stop me wanting to lob the scales out of the bathroom window. Not that I'm an aggressive gay, you understand.

DAY FIVE: I kid you not, I am actually feeling so much purer inside. (My body, not my mind.) I doubt that'll ever be pure. Especially after my visit to the Turkish bath. But I feel I may need some anger management sessions soon. You see, Saturday's are normally my cake and wine day. (Well, that has actually been most days recently but Saturday's especially.) So there I was getting really excited about the prospect of Belgian bun and bottle of Sauvignon I was going to consume when it hit me. Like a ruddy great lightning bolt. I'm on a detox.

DAY SIX: After an awfully stressful day at work, I made a conscious decision. I need a glass of Sauvignon Blanc. No, not a glass. A whole bottle. I popped into my little Tesco Express and picked up a bottle. I lashed myself on my faux leather sofa, put on my Prisoner: Cell Block H DVD (so gay, I know) and drank the whole bottle. I'm clearly as successful with detoxing as I am dating.

Chapter Thirty-One

That time I lost my erection (January 2009)

I t certainly makes me feel like I've had an extremely action-packed life when it comes to matters of the heart and the bedroom. My friends always tell me my antics make for wonderful dinner party stories. I'm glad I keep them and their guests entertained.

This one particular night, Tullene and I were going out to celebrate. I don't really know what we were celebrating. Seeing as we were only 24, it was probably a celebration of being paid.

It was a time when The Bill was still on the box. So I had to set the VCR to record because Tullene was dragging me out on a school night. I can't be bothered to explain what a VCR is to younger readers. But it was the olden day version of having a Sky box.

Oh, how I love The Bill. Anyone who knows me will know what an über fan of The Bill I was and still am. Never missed an episode. And now I have the whole series in my DVD collection. And I still watch it every day, now it is being repeated on the Drama channel. Maybe I shouldn't admit to this. It may make me even more Undateable, but sod it, I'm getting too old to care what people think.

Such a fan was I, that my quote of the 90s and the 00s was, "Next time on the Bill." I used to say it at every opportunity I got. If a friend announced a pregnancy or whatever, I'd do my mock shocked face and scream, "Next time on the Bill!" The only time I don't think it was appreciated was when my friend's nan had just died. Oh well, I was just trying to lighten the mood.

We arrived in Reflex to splash our wages. God, that takes me back. Reflex in Kingston. R.I.P. What a shame it no longer exists. Too many outer London gay venues are closing for my liking.

So here we were in the dearly departed Reflex and this man approached me. He wasn't exactly the prettiest grape in the bunch but my beer goggles were well and truly attached to my old pork pies by this point.

I hadn't had a drunken snog in ages and he supplied some lip servicing. I heard Tullene, you know her by now, I heard her shout: "NEXT TIME ON THE BILL" as our lips locked. I burst out laughing in the poor boy's mouth.

As he questioned our bizarre behaviour, which actually most people do when it comes to Tullene and I, he asked what the hell we were going on about. I enthusiastically filled him in on my love story with The Bill, at which point he whipped out his warrant card.

Fuck a duck, he was only a real-life police officer. I was as hard as a truncheon.

Before you could say, "Next time on the Bill", I was back at the police officer's house. He had suddenly become a lot more attractive. I couldn't believe I was about to have sexual relations with a real police officer.

I opened his wardrobe to check there was a uniform inside. He could have been lying to me, just to lure me back to have his wicked way. All the episodes of The Bill I had watched had clearly given me a suspicious mind.

We got on the bed and as we got our clothes off, I noticed it wasn't only his face that had been at the back of the queue when looks were being dished out. My truncheon seemed to lose its life. It went down like a popped balloon. The first time in my whole life, I had lost my erection. The sheer embarrassment.

I blame it on Karma. Never should you be so fickle and shag a man based on their job. Please make sure you fancy them. I picked up my clothes and did a runner. NEXT TIME ON THE BILL...

Chapter Thirty-Two

The Lucky Escape- when your date turns out to be a thug (July 2009)

After seeing a therapist who was treating me for my erectile dysfunction, I was just about to graduate from university. I didn't venture far from home for my degree. I attended Brunel in the, how can I put this delicately, slightly dodgy area of Uxbridge. I've always been a bit of a homebird you see, or as some would say, a Mummy's boy.

To get me through my degree (and to keep me in Savvy B), I had a job in a lovely little gay pub. I'd decided a full-time position in prostitution wasn't for me. The Culvert it was called. Some of you may remember it. It's no longer there unfortunately, which is very sad as it was always such a busy pub. But alas, *this is the way a lot of the local gay pubs are going*. R.I.P. The Culvert.

Being the young, cock hungry gay boy that I was, and still am, this was the perfect job for me. It was like being an obese bloke in a cake shop. So many to choose from but which one to choose?

This one night, a very handsome bloke caught my eye. My god, I can remember him like it was yesterday. He was drop dead gorgeous. He had a mop of curly brown hair and the most dazzling brown eyes. But alas, he appeared to be straight.

It was quite common to get straights in the pub. They often came for a quiet pint or they were accompanying a gaggle of gay mates. But oh well, I thought, at least it gives me a bit of eye candy for the evening. Some people call it perving, I call it appreciating fine art.

Well, to my surprise, when I approached this straight, handsome man to take his drink order, he placed his hand on top of mine and seductively asked for a pint of Stella. My eyes nearly popped out of their sockets as he stroked my hand.

I pulled my hand away from his stroke and I came over all unnecessary. I started to pull his pint, hoping it wouldn't be the only thing I was pulling that evening.

I lost all concentration. I couldn't take my eyes off him. His pint of Stella frothed over rather dramatically and dribbled down my trousers. Well, I think it was the Stella that was dribbling down my trousers.

I felt my face flush. I mean, not that you could tell as I was well and truly fake tanned up.

"I hope that's not the only spillage I witness tonight!", this cheeky handsome chappy shouted across the bar.

As I handed him his dripping pint of Stella, I felt a bit of sweat on my brow. Panicking I'd have a streaky fake tan moment, I quickly dabbed it and he held out his hand. I shook it.

"Aaron", he introduced himself.

"I've not seen you here before." I started the conversation.

"I'm visiting from Windsor."

He's a long way from home, I thought. Especially for a pint of Stella.

"You're beautiful!" He told me. Sweet talking me he was, but boy did it work. I was putty in his hands.

"Thank you." Uncharacteristically, I went shy.

He stayed standing at the bar all evening, not taking his eyes off me. We made lots of conversation, getting to know each other.

"Do you live local?" He enquired.

"Just around the corner", I replied.

"Not far for US to go after you've finished then."

How forward, I thought to myself. Not that I was opposed to the idea, you understand. The answer would certainly be yes. This fit, handsome stranger was definitely coming back to my house.

As closing time approached, I could feel a little movement beginning in my trouser department. Mini Mark was getting a little excited at the thought of a night of passion with the man from Windsor.

I rang the final bell to announce it was last orders. That was always my favourite part of working in a pub. It made me feel like I was Peggy Mitchell.

"GET OUT OF MY PUB!" I used to shout sporadically, for no reason whatsoever.

"I'll wait for you outside", said the Windsor fitty as he leant over the bar and attached his lips to mine. Yes, he kissed me.

My tongue hung out the corner of my lip and drooped down to my chin, Beethoven style, as I watched him walk outside.

I don't think I've ever mopped a floor as quickly as I did that night. I was like Mr Muscle on speed. Desperate to get out of that pub and make my way into this boy's boxers.

As I said goodnight to my colleagues, I rushed out the door and got the shock of my life. I arrived outside just in time to see my potential shag being bundled into a police car. My jaw dropped quicker than a whore's drawers. I saw Aaron look up at me as the police officer pushed him inside the car, his hand on his head.

In complete shock, still catching flies, I looked up at the bouncer.

"What happened to that boy?"

"He came out and accused one of the regulars of staring at him, called him a poof and then punched him!"

My eyes widened. I went home on my own that night and have never been so glad to have missed out on a shag.

Chapter Thirty-Three

The issue of having a high sex drive
(September 2009)

I remember George. Now he was a handsome sort. And he wasn't just a one-night stand actually. Oh no. We had sex on numerous occasions over the course of a few months. I suppose you would call him a fuck buddy.

Any ex-boyfriend of mine who might be reading will tell you – I have an incredibly high sex drive. After I cum, just give me ten minutes to have a wee and a suck on my vape and I can go again. No problem.

Except this did turn out to be a problem for George, who couldn't keep up with me. And one night (after we'd made love FOUR times), he got up from the bed, slightly limp and informed me he wouldn't be able to see me again. And so I was dumped by my FB for having a high sex drive.

Chapter Thirty-Four

Can you find love at the work Christmas do?
(December 2009)

I remember Tullene asking me to be her plus one at her work's Christmas function. I was reluctant to go after my brush with a homophobic bash artist, but Tullene gave me some reassuring words of advice. Should have been a counsellor, that girl. And yes, that is sarcasm.

"Just because you nearly shagged a gay basher, doesn't mean the same will happen to you at my work's Christmas party!" FAMOUS LAST WORDS.

You probably all know Tullene by now. And for those of you who are unfortunate enough to... whoops slip of the keyboard. I meant, for those of you who are FORTUNATE enough to, I'm sure you'll be questioning why I said yes. Drama follows that girl and me.

My initial question was "Why can't you take your boyfriend?" To which she replied, "I can't take my boyfriend because he got into a fight last year and now he's barred from all work functions."

My gut instinct should have been to decline the invitation. I hesitated suddenly, and was about to make my excuses, when Tullene pulled out her trump card.

"There's a very handsome gay man that's just started working with me."

My ears pricked up. Oh, who am I to turn down an invitation to a social gathering? It is Christmas after all. And I may also find a pot of gold at the end of the rainbow.

Before I could mutter the words, Christmas work do, I found myself sat at a very posh table at a hotel in Heathrow. I'd dug out my best all-in-one grey suit, and as I had, some moths flew towards me. I hadn't had any cause to wear it in recent years. I'm at an age now where everyone in my social circle has got married. Except for me, that is. I'm still the token single friend.

But before anyone breaks out the violins, let's get back to the works do. Tullene had slyly juggled with the place settings and I had conveniently ended up sitting next to the new gay boy colleague she had previously mentioned.

I was about to abuse Tullene by bellowing Cilla Black across the table at her but my eyes came out on storks as Dave, that's his name, approached the table and came to take his place next to me. HANDSOME was an understatement. I had to pick up the swan-shaped napkin from the table to dab up the dribble from my watering mouth.

We got on famously. We laughed, we joked and we innuen-doed our way through the three-course meal. I could see Tullene's eyes light up as she oozed with pride that her Cilla Black attempts were appearing to be successful.

As the coffee was being poured, he stood up and asked if I'd like to dance. Oh, it was so romantic. And so old fashioned. I loved it. I stood up quicker than a bolt of lightning.

He took my hand and led me to the dancefloor. It was like a

scene out of a cheesy 80's soap. And for those who know me best, will know that that is right up my street.

All my friends tell me I was born in the wrong decade. I love anything 80's, or 90's come to that. My DVD collection consists of nostalgic soaps and drama series. Prisoner: Cell Block H, Take the High Road, Dynasty, Howard's Way. The list goes on.

Anyway, enough of the nostalgic digression. Back to the dancefloor.

As Dave lifted me up into the air, Dirty Dancing style, I felt a flutter. Well, he didn't actually lift me up into the air. I just made that bit up. I thought it made it sound more romantic. And to be honest, I don't think anyone could actually lift me up. I've come to adore Savvy B and cake too much.

But as he span me around, he leant over and whispered into my ear.

"Would you like to come for a glass of wine up in my room?"

Now, you know me, I'm not normally so easy when I've just met a guy but who was I to turn down a handsome man? Or wine? And after all, it is Christmas. I thought it could be my present to myself.

I surveyed the room, looking for Tullene but she was nowhere to be seen. Dave grabbed my hand and led the way.

As I was being led by my Christmas present, I saw a group of Tullene's colleagues in the corner, and suddenly my ears pricked up.

"POOFS!" I heard one of them shout. My nostrils flared and I felt steam coming from my ears.

"Ignore them!" Dave pleaded as he tried to drag me on. But I simply couldn't ignore it. Not blatant homophobia. I'm not really a fighter and I normally avoid confrontation like the plague, but that comment had really got my goat up.

I managed to escape Dave's hand and I marched up to the

perpetrator of the comment. Looking him straight in the eye, I wracked my brains for a suitable, intellectual comeback.

"And you're a cunt!" Well, it was the best I could muster. Straight, direct and to the point.

He looked shocked as I took Dave's hand and we continued on our journey to Dave's room. Maybe he didn't expect this POOF to respond. I inhaled a deep breath and pushed my chest out. I felt liberated.

As we made our way to the lifts, I heard a man's voice shout "OI!" I quickly span around in my shiny loafers. It was the homophobe.

"What did you call me?" he barked in my face. He was clearly deaf as well as a C U Next Tuesday. So, I repeated my offensive comeback just to ensure there was no misunderstanding as to what I'd said.

And next, well, I don't know what came over me but I could smell danger. I feared he was about to punch me so I decided I should be the one to make the first move. Before you could say, Merry Christmas, I seemed to have my hand gripped around his throat and I pushed him up against the wall.

"MARK!" I heard Tullene's voice come out of nowhere. "What the hell are you doing?"

Now, for those who know Tullene, know that she has a very bad, violent temper. Especially when she sees her friends in danger. I knew I had to rile her up quickly as I feared I needed her help. I may have had my hand around his throat but I didn't actually know what my next move was going to be. I'd never punched anyone in my whole life.

"He called me a poof!" I screamed. I saw the top of Tullene's head pop open with steam. And I saw Tullene's eyes change to angry Tullene.

"WHAT?" She bellowed. I felt the man's Adam apple as he gulped.

He tried to deny it but Tullene was having none of it. She lifted up her crutch. No, I'm not talking about her lady garden. An actual crutch. Now, for anyone wondering where this random crutch appeared from, let me tell you.

Tullene has a weak ankle. Along with various other ailments and conditions which I won't bore you with. She bores us enough with them! But anyway, she broke her ankle at my 25th birthday party. And that's a story for another time!

She picked up her crutch and whacked the man behind his legs. He fell out of my grip and dropped to the floor, legs akimbo.

"That's for being a cunt! And homophobic!" She screamed and dragged me into the lift out of harm's way. In all the commotion, I hadn't noticed Dave had gone missing. Maybe he was scared of my fight club impression. So I never made it up to Dave's hotel room. But at least I stood up to a homophobe!

I also hasten to add, Tullene had to find someone else to take to the next year's Christmas do.

Chapter Thirty-Five

My passionate lover (February 2010)

Then there was AJ. A very beautiful Australian bloke. He was such a tentative, seductive and attentive shag. As we were between the sheets, I felt like we were performing a sex scene from 80's super soap, *DYNASTY*.

And I couldn't help but declare my satisfaction. Mid-way through love making, I stopped, grabbed his face and declared:

"You're such a passionate lover!" A la Joan Collins style.

And when I say Joan Collins. I mean it. I imitated her accent, seductive purr and glamorous pout to a tee. I was so proud. He was less impressed with my impersonation. He quickly finished and made his excuses to leave, never to be heard of again.

Chapter Thirty-Six

That date when I was arrested for being drunk and disorderly (August 2010)

You would have thought that I'd learnt my lesson about finding true love by now. But no, ever the glutton for punishment, when my latest beau, Kevin suggested a day trip to Brighton, I jumped at the chance.

Kevin was/is the son of my then hairdresser. I say was as he's no longer in my life and his mum no longer puts a pair of scissors anywhere near my bonce.

This one day, she was chopping away at my rather thinning hair and she started talking about Kevin. Although I knew she had a gay son, I'd never met him.

"Oh Mark. My Kevin's just split up with his fella. He could do with cheering up."

Alarm bells should have immediately started ringing in my ears. REBOUND. But this is me after all and I'm never one for saying no. In fact, NO has always been a word that struggles to leave my lips. Perhaps that's why certain people have called me a slut over the years.

No sooner had the words, "Okay, I'd love to meet him" left my gob, this tall, jaw droppingly handsome man appeared from behind the door.

She was either a magician or this had been a planned set up. Seeing his gorgeous flop of brown hair and deep-set green eyes quickly made me erase all thoughts of my hairdressers' wizardry. Either that, or she'd wiped out my memory with another spell of black magic.

We caught each other's eyes and I recognised a glint in both his and mine. I smiled and I witnessed him become rather dazzled at the sight of my pearly whites. I'd been to the hygienist that particular day for a clean and polish.

"Do you fancy a day trip to Brighton?" He forwardly asked me.

"Damn right!" I blurted out quicker than you could say pier.

Before I knew it, we were at Euston waiting for the twelve minutes past ten fast train. We chatted with ease and laughed a lot. We had the same stupid sense of humour.

I soon found a glass of Sauvignon Blanc from the train's buffet table and it was going down a treat. Luckily, he shared my love of all things Savvy B. Except he appeared to love it much more than me. He was already on his second glass before I was even half way through my first.

But, as you know, the good Catholic boy that I am, I shalt not judge.

No sooner were we off the train, Kevin had his lips firmly plastered around another glass of Savvy B inside The Queen's Arms. My eyes widened as I saw him pour the wine down his gullet quicker than Jaws approaching a surf board.

As my friends quite often say, "if Mark is shocked by some-one's behaviour, then that's saying something". It MUST be shocking. Now, until I spent some time with Kevin, I thought that

I could put the Savvy B away. But he made me look like a tee-total monk.

After God knows how many glasses in The Queen's Arms, he suggested we take a walk along the pier. Well, I say walk. By this point, it was more of a stumble.

Stumbling along the pier, we ventured into the arcade. As we came out the other side, Kevin grabbed my hand with excitement. How romantic, I thought, the way he's clutching at my hand with such enthusiasm. It soon became clear that the overzealous way he held my hand had more to do with the pub on the pier he had spotted and was now dragging me into.

Five more glasses of vino for Kevin and just two more for me, I was struggling to keep up. I suggested we get some sea air. I thought it might help sober us up, if nothing else.

As we ventured out onto Brighton sea front, I turned to look at the pier all lit up. What a beautiful sight. Suddenly confused, I turned to look at Kevin who seemed to be sporting two heads.

"I didn't know there were two piers!" God knows how I was managing to string a sentence together.

"There is only one pier", Kevin told me, "The other one burnt down in the eighties."

With hindsight, I realise the copious amounts of Sauvignon Blanc had probably started to affect my vision.

"Revenge should be open by now!" Kevin grabbed my hand rather enthusiastically. The fact that I struggled to put one foot in front of the other should have been a massive hint that I was ready to get the train back to London.

Just as we went to cross the road, a policeman tapped me on the shoulder. My head flopping from side to side, I managed to turn to face him without falling flat on my boatrace.

"Don't you think it's time you called it a night." P.C Plod advised, obviously observing my inebriated state.

Wanting to nod my head, I didn't get a chance to respond as Kevin took the lead.

"The night is only just beginning!"

"It looks like it began a long while ago!"

I do like a policeman with a sense of humour.

Ignoring the officer of the law, Kevin took my hand once more and started to pull me away from P.C Plod. Struggling to stay in an upright position, I found myself clinging onto the policeman's shirt.

And before you could say, Old Bill, I had fallen to the pavement, pulling P.C Plod on top of me. And then, just to put the icing on the cake, the Savvy B (and empty stomach) finally caught up with Kevin. I saw projectile vomit launch towards us.

"I'm arresting you both for being drunk and disorderly in a public place."

Those were the last words I heard before my eyes opened again in the cold light of day. Sunshine beaming through police cell bars.

I got the train home to London all on my own.

Receiving a caution on a date was a sure-fire way to ensure that a second date with Kevin was definitely not on the cards.

Chapter Thirty-Seven

Can you find love in a gay sauna? (Sometime shortly after getting a criminal record)

I decided that I deserved a relaxing day after my brush with the law. Spa day.

As my quest for Mr Right continued, I was keeping an open mind when it comes to ways of discovering just where the bloody hell he is. Because right then, he was completely UTL. Does Mr Right even exist? Is there really such a thing? Bugger me, I'm procrastinating and counselling myself as I write.

So, as I sipped on an ice-cold glass of Sauvignon in an empty gay pub in the heart of Uxbridge, (no wonder it's empty, it's Uxbridge!), I overheard some rather slutty looking queens talking about a sauna in Soho. And they said it's such a great place to meet men. My ears pricked up like a cat's tail once they've seen a mouse.

Wonderful, I thought to myself, that's where I can meet the man of my dreams, my Mr Right, the man I'm meant to share my living days with; in a sauna.

I wasted no time; before you could blink, I'd knocked back the Savvy B and was at the entrance of this sauna. I remember it being bloody dark. Cor, my old apple pies ain't the best in daylight, let alone in that dimly lit setting. I've needed glasses since a very young age.

Luckily, I had my contact lenses in so it was only the darkness I had to contend with. I was so excited for my sauna experience. I thought to myself, even if I don't meet a man, it was still going to be a relaxing and rejuvenating evening.

I entered the locker rooms and saw men walking around in their birthday suits. I went into a sheer panic.

I couldn't possibly walk around in mine. I grabbed a rescue remedy pastille from my Superdry bag and sucked on it. I needed it to calm my nerves. I've always got pills in my bag for any eventuality. My friends call me a walking pharmacy. If you've got the shits, a bad head, feeling sick or you just need a vitamin boost, I've got the solution.

After sucking on my pastille for a few moments and giving myself a good old slap round my Botox-ed boat race, I told myself that I'm a young, attractive gay boy and I can walk around naked! And I thanked God I'd stuck to my New Year's resolution of swimming. I've got biceps that would make Tom Daley swoon. So off came my clothes and I opened the door.

Once in the sauna, I saw a man's genitalia, practically staring me in the eye. He was naked with a boner, in this sauna. What a saucy minx.

We were practically eye to eye and I'm talking the eye on my face and his special downstairs eye. Cor, I bet that hurts, I found myself thinking. He winked at me. With the eye on his face, I'd just like to point out. I shyly said hello. He just shook his head to the left and walked off into a locker. Well, it looked like a locker. But it was bigger, and had a black bench in it that looked like a bed.

Maybe he's feeling sleepy. Fucking rude, though, I thought.

What was the point of winking at me? And then just walking off? I shouldn't be too judgemental, though, maybe he had a nervous twitch.

I decided to find the jacuzzi. Oh yes, that'd be bloody lovely. A warm bubbly bath to soothe my achy muscles after a 70 length breaststroke marathon in the pool. I saw two old men sitting in the jacuzzi, I mean they must have been at least 75. I glanced up and saw a walking stick hanging from one of the hooks. Bless them. At least they still get out the house and look after themselves. I smiled at them as I got in, which as you will discover, was my downfall.

As I sat my naked body down in the jacuzzi, the two geriatrics started to grin at me with their false gnashers. I mean, I didn't know for definite that they had false ones, I'm just being ageist. I laid back and closed my eyes, enjoying the bubbles fizzing around me. Cor, I suddenly felt bubbles bubbling quite ferociously around my man bits. I started to feel slightly aroused from jacuzzi fizz and I put my hand down to check it wasn't being fizzed away from my pubic bone. And my lord, I got a shock.

My hand bumped into another hand and I looked up, and I saw the geriatric grinning at me, a full display of false Steradent cleaned gnashers glistening in my apple pies. At least his false teeth aren't stained, I thought to myself. So, it could have been worse.

He had got his bloody hand on my penis. The dirty old perve. I was old enough to be his great grandson. I protested and attempted to pull away but he grabbed my leg and pulled me towards him. Cor, he was strong for an old bugger.

"Now, I'm not really interested!" I started to protest.

"Oh, come on! Make an old man happy!" He seedily said.

"No, I will not!"

Well, as I went to stand and get out from the jacuzzi, he

pulled me towards him so fast that I slipped off the seat, screaming as I went, and my head slipped under the water. And I could still feel the bloody old bugger's hand on my manhood. But right then, I was more annoyed that my whole head and hair were under the water and wet. I finally managed to pull myself from his grip and I stormed out the jacuzzi. And out of the sauna. I don't think that was the right place to look for love...

Chapter Thirty-Eight

The time I decided to go on THAT Channel four show- FIRST DATES (July 2011)

After having successive failed dates, I thought I'd try my luck in the First Dates restaurant. What did I have to lose?

In my opening interview, I proclaimed on national television that I'm a really horny person and if I see a fit man on the tube, I get a tent pole and have to cover my crotch with my man bag. Great start.

It was a boiling hot day and as I walked into the restaurant, I was sweating like a Bombay hooker. I chose to wear a pair of shorts, hoping it wouldn't look too casual. But to my relief, my date Lee, was also in shorts. Phew, I thought, we can both look casual together. Another bloody Lee, but at least this one had decent teeth.

I was escorted to meet Lee by the maître d' and we awkwardly introduced ourselves. We clearly didn't know whether we should shake hands or share a kiss on the cheek. After nearly head butting each other, we settled on the kiss on the cheek.

We instantly found we had some common ground, discovering that we'd both worked as entertainers for holiday parks. The other mutual trait we shared were perfectly plucked pruned eyebrows. This put me off straight away as I usually like my men a bit more rugged and less manicured. I WANT to be the pretty one in a relationship.

No surprises, I was instantly knocking back the Sauvignon Blanc. And I went straight in for direct questioning. No point beating around the bush, I always say.

In fact, I never beat around the bush.

Hence the fact I'm gay.

Direct and to the point, that's me. Just call me Jack Bauer.

"So... are you looking for a long term relationship?" I asked.

Maybe a little forward for the first conversation but I do like to know where I stand. Even though I didn't fancy Lee on first sight, I like to keep an open mind. You never know if the spark will come later.

The conversation quickly moved onto kids and we both agreed we would want a boy if we were to have children.

"I'd want a boy because girls are bitches!" I declared, whilst looking around for my Savvy B to be topped up.

As I swigged some more of the First Dates restaurant's Savvy B, for some reason I decided it would be a good idea to tell my date that I've already got my wedding planned. And no word of a lie, this is what I have envisaged all of my life.

I want the vicar to come up from under the pulpit on a revolving platform. And I want a disco ball spinning as I make my way down the aisle. And the best bit; my walk-in song is Whitney Houston classic, 'How will I know?', if he really loves me, I say a prayer with every heartbeat".

Really proud that I'd clearly described my wedding, I see Lee has fallen deadly silent, lost for words. A rarity with this man, let me tell you, as he loved the sound of his own voice.

Breaking the silence, I asked, "Does it sound like a wedding for which you'd like to be the fellow groom for?"

"NO", he bluntly replied, "It sounds really tacky."

My face drops as I knock back some more wine and another deathly silence fills the table. Well, I guess I did ask.

To break the silence, Lee asked if we should go for a cigarette. Relieved that we both smoke, I jumped at the chance to grab a nicotine fix after failing to woo him with my wedding plans.

As we puffed on our Mayfair fags (yes, classy I know), the conversation turned to our coming out stories. I came out to the world at 17, even though I don't actually think I really needed to tell anyone because they'd all guessed that I was a raging homo. Actually, I don't know if guessed is the right word. It just so happens that none of my friends and family are blind or deaf.

Discussing our school years, I opened up about being bullied. God, now I know I'm quite an open and honest person but I don't think I'd ever been quite so open and honest on a date before.

Once upon a time, I was held down on the school field by some boys who wrote "Faggot" on my forehead in black marker pen. Yes, sad but a true story. And then I was the one who got into trouble with the Headmaster. YES, ME! He told me off for having pen on my face which wasn't in accordance with the school uniform policy. What a bastard, although this was the 1990s. If that were to happen in this day and age, the Headmaster would get sacked for sure.

Nicotine fix completed, we were back at the table, being served our mains when... Cue another awkward silence as I bring up the fact I had quite a religious upbringing. Believe it or not, I went to Sunday school and I was in the church choir. And I still regularly go to church now.

"So have you never been to church?" I enquired.

"I go for like christenings, weddings, just when I've got to", was his response.

As the conversation evolved, I fear I was a little too defensive of my old mate Jesus. After Lee called the communion wine, rancid old vinegar, I proclaimed:

"I can't believe you just dissed Jesus' blood!"

That quote will follow me around for years to come as I saw it quoted on Twitter hundreds of times the night the programme went to air.

"Maybe we shouldn't discuss religion", I sensibly suggested as I grabbed the waiter's attention to get some more wine. And no, I didn't ask for rancid old vinegar.

Note to self: Don't talk about religion, wedding plans or being bullied on first dates. It creates too many awkward silences.

During my closing interview, the producers were plying me with wine. Trying to get me pissed they were. Attempting to loosen my lips even more so than they usually are.

I proclaimed that I didn't really fancy him but if there was the option, I'd probably go home to bed with him.

SLUT.

I think our final conversation on camera summed up our date perfectly.

LEE: I think you're really nice. BUT... we are too alike personality wise.

ME: It would be like shagging myself if I shagged you.

LEE: Just a better-looking version.

Cue my pursed lips.

Even television can't guarantee this undateable gay a future of love. Maybe I should try Blind Date next...

Chapter Thirty-Nine

My sexual assault (A week after FIRST DATES)

After appearing on national television in my search for love, I became quite the Twitter celebrity. I felt quite famous whilst walking down the street one day and someone shouted, "FIRST DATES!" at me. I was less impressed when someone tweeted "That Mark's eyebrows look like slugs above his eyes." The bare faced cheek.

People found out I was a massage therapist so I'd been using my fifteen minutes of fame to coin in some extra money from new clients. They all wanted that boy who had been on the telly to give them a rub down.

I'd been called to a client's flat in Regents Park. I'd never treated this particular client before so he was a stranger to me. But I do remember that his name was Joe. And his face will haunt me for the rest of my life.

He was in his 50's with a strong Mediterranean accent. I'm not certain it was his real accent; he could have been putting on a voice for all I knew. But I remember him being bald with very weathered skin. I came to the conclusion that he'd been a sun worshipper in his time. That's all I can remember of his physical appearance.

I can remember the day though as if it were only yesterday. Although on the other hand, I've also blocked it out and it feels just like a bad nightmare I had one night. It seems really hazy in my mind but also really vivid all at the same time.

I arrived and walked into his apartment and he closed the door behind us. As a person, I believe I'm quite intuitive, because as soon as I was inside, I felt something wasn't quite right. He barked at me in his Mediterranean accent to take my clothes off. I was a little taken aback and explained that I keep my clothes on to perform massage. He was angry at my response and immediately pushed me onto his bed.

The next thing I remember is feeling helpless as he ripped off my t shirt and pulled down my trousers. I'm quite a strong man but I felt it was safer not to fight him. He started touching my penis and then he put it into his mouth. I could see him getting angry because I wasn't getting aroused and my penis was staying in its flaccid state.

He then decided to pull his trousers down, he was fully erect and viciously shoved his penis into my mouth and forced me to perform oral sex on him. I tried to push him off but he just put his hand around my throat. I felt completely powerless and decided the best course of action was to just give him what he wanted. I felt a tear come into my eye but I decided that I wasn't going to give this bastard the satisfaction of seeing me cry.

He finally ejaculated after what seemed a lifetime and loosened his grip of my throat. As he got up, he threw £40 at me. And then he shouted at me to get dressed and get out. Not only had he sexually assaulted me, he'd treated me like a prostitute. I now felt violated. And cheap. And scared. I got out of there as quickly as I could. I just drove away from his house at the speed of lighting.

Looking back, I wished I'd gone straight to the police station and reported him for sexually assaulting me. But for a number of reasons, I decided against it. The stigma surrounding gay men is that of promiscuity. I thought people would think, oh he's gay, he obviously went on Grindr looking for it.

I also had the bizarre misconception that assaults and rape can only happen to women. I thought by admitting to what had happened to me would make me look like a weak person. I've got an exceptionally strong and loud personality. I thought there was no way anyone would believe this could happen to me. Surely these things can only happen to people with weaker or quieter personalities. How wrong was I?

I now know I should have gone to the police. I carry the guilt around with me that my failure to report him could have led to more sexual assaults on other innocent victims. If I could go back in time, I would like to see my attacker brought to justice for the violation he subjected me to.

Chapter Forty

And here's why you should never fake tan while flaccid (Valentine's Day 2012)

It took a good few months after Joe to even want to talk to a man again, let alone date one. But I decided I wasn't going to let that bastard rule my life. He was no longer going to have power over me. And I made the decision that Valentine's Day was the perfect opportunity.

I've never been a fan of Valentine's Day. Lots of couples going out for expensive dinners. Idiots. I decided that I was a strong, independent gay man who needed no-one. I'd resigned myself to the fact that no cards from eligible bachelors were going to be gracing my letterbox. No flowers delivered from florists were going to be displayed on my window sill. Oh Jesus, someone get the violins out and a bottle of Prozac.

I must tell you that I did send one card though. And that was to my dear devoted mummy. The sheer embarrassment in the shop when the sales assistant asked, "ooh, who's the lucky man?" whilst fondling the card which read, I LOVE YOU. Holding up my head (and my chins), I said, "It's for my Mum actually!" I thought I was going to throttle the bitch as she pulled her glasses down her nose to look at me and bite her lip sympathetically.

I could see it in her eyes, the look of sheer sympathy. I could read her thoughts. The poor bachelor gay boy in his late twenties, whose face won't move for Botox and who's spent more time drinking Sauvignon Blanc than he has been in relationships.

Well, that's what her face said but the words that actually left her mouth were:

"I hope I have a son like you one day!"

Anyway, enough of my Valentine's card woes. Even though I'd decided I didn't need a relationship, a man for shagging purposes might be nice. So, I went to visit a dear old friend, affectionately known as an FB. I won't explain FB in case my mum is reading. She'll just think it stands for Facebook so let's just leave it at that.

Preparation for a visit to the FB is crucial. Out came my tube of Veet and the manscaping commenced. Next was a visit to the spray tan booth. I whipped off my clothes and let the rays of fake sun, otherwise known as Lauren's way, penetrate me from head to toe. You must always have a spray tan completely naked. You can't risk any potential white bits.

Hair free and sun-kissed, I was ready for Mr FB. It was time to build up my strength for a night of Valentine's passion so out came the spinach and the rocket. I gobbled my way through the meal and off I went. Just call me Popeye.

As the passion began, we ripped each other's clothes off. I'm fearing this tale is going to turn into a snippet from a Mills & Boon. But so be it, the needs of telling this story demand it sounds so.

Now, for any man who knows me intimately, will know it doesn't take me long before my manhood stands to full attention. A red-blooded man, Kylie would sing.

As Mr FB went to attend to my man soldier, I saw his eyes widen.

"What?" I screamed.

"Have you got some sort of skin condition?" he asked.

It was time for my eyes to widen.

"No! I fucking don't!" I bellowed.

He instructed me to look at my erected soldier and as I did, my eyes widened even wider. Cor! Where I'd had the spray tan naked with a flaccid penis, it clearly hadn't fake tanned all the skin. My erect penis had stripes!

"You've got a Zebra penis!" Mr FB thought it was funny. If only it was the size of a Zebras.

To quickly move on from the sheer embarrassment of the Zebra situation, I held Mr FB down and performed fellatio. I'm using that posh word in case my mum is reading. She'll think it's a character from a Shakespeare play.

As I pulled away from my act of fellatio, I noticed a bit of rocket dangling from the end of Mr FB's manhood.

OH GOD, PLEASE GROUND, SWALLOW ME NOW! Normally it's me that's doing the swallowing.

Mr FB looked up, or I should say down actually and he noticed the rocket dangling.

"Where did that come from?" I asked innocently.

I decided I should avoid sexual encounters as well as relationships. And so I made a New Year's resolution, there and then, to do just that. Well, not quite New Year as it was February. But you get the gist.

Chapter Forty-One

Don't let a scorned beauty therapist wax your brows (July 2012)

Never one for sticking to New Year's resolutions, I was soon back in the dating game. Call me a hopeless romantic, if you will. Or just a slut.

JAMIE. He was my next attempt at a happily ever after.

He came along in a time when I had quite an addiction to Grindr. At one point, I thought I was going to need therapy to wean myself off the app. I deleted it after Jamie. But that's not to say it will never be downloaded again.

But one night, (before it was deleted) I was just finishing work and I fancied a bit of jiggy jiggy and a glass of wine. So, I turned on Grindr and waited for a ping.

I never initiate a conversation on this app. Call it fear of rejection or whatever you like. But just as I was taking a sip of Savvy B, a message pinged up.

It was a very handsome man, in his late 30s and he lived in Weybridge. My antennae started whizzing around. Oooh, I thought. An older man is just what I need. He'll be mature and experienced, I thought. And he lived in Weybridge, so I assumed he would be rich, even more appealing.

Before you could say blow job, Jamie had invited me over to his gaff for a glass of Savvy B. Which we all know is secret code for sex. Well, maybe not so secret.

Pardon the pun, but when I walked in, he really blew my mind. Along with something else.

It felt different with Jamie. For anyone not in the know about Grindr, you normally walk straight through the front door and then, more often than not, you head straight to the bedroom.

But not with Jamie. He already had a glass of plonk waiting for me and told me to take a seat on the sofa. We actually got on really well and I could feel my heart skip a beat as he looked at me as we laughed.

After two glasses of Savvy B, he came in for the kiss. Obviously, it would have been rude of me not to reciprocate. There was a real passion in the way he kissed me and before you could say anal, he had dragged me into the bedroom. Not that I needed much dragging.

I pulled down his trousers and I nearly fainted. His penis was already fully erect so as it escaped from his flies, it came at my face like a coiled spring. I had to dodge it otherwise I fear I may have been blinded in my right eye.

And I hate to be crude, but my word, it was rather large. I do believe I could have used it as a rolling pin.

As I stripped off my clothes, I saw him lean over and open his bedside drawer. When I saw him pull out a pair of handcuffs, I think I turned white.

You all know by now my complete obsession and love of the well-known TV show The Bill.

But even so, I didn't know how I felt about being handcuffed to a bed.

Before you could shout, "Arrest that man!", he had hand-cuffed me to the bed. I actually found it all quite exhilarating.

We had an hour of passionate lovemaking. I call it lovemaking as, contrary to popular belief, I really am a hopeless romantic. After the deed was done, he released me from the cuffs and I kissed him goodnight. As I drove away, I hoped he would ask to see me again.

A few weeks went by and we had started to see each other on a regular basis. Although it was only for sex. I'd become quite accustomed to being handcuffed. I used to scream, Next Time on The Bill!

We never left the house together or went to a restaurant or anywhere in public actually. It was just sex. But I had started to fall in love with my fuck buddy. Oh shit. What a big faux pas.

On numerous occasions, I begged him to take things to the next level.

"Why don't you take me out for dinner?" He would always fob me off when I asked that question.

"I'm tired." Not too tired for sex, I used to think. Not that I was complaining, it was very passionate and I enjoyed it. He'd even taught me the orgasmic joy of licking an armpit.

One day, after quite a few months of handcuffed lovemaking, I insisted that I would be round on Monday when he finished work, to cook him a lovely home cooked meal. If he couldn't take me out for dinner because he was too tired, I would bring the dinner to him!

I gauged his reaction and, considering he'd never tasted my cooking, I could tell he wasn't keen on the idea. And then he came out with it.

"I think you want more from me than I want to give you."

OH. My face dropped. Obviously not literally. I've had far too much Botox for that to happen. But you get the picture.

"But you keep asking me back", I was ashamed at how needy I sounded.

"Yes, but I just want sex."

Heartbroken. I walked out of his flat, taking my half drunken bottle of Sauvignon Blanc with me. I felt no desire to share my expensive New Zealand wine with that bastard.

A year had passed me by and Jamie hadn't entered my thoughts in a while. Until one day, when a message popped up in my inbox.

"Do you still do beauty treatments? I need my eyebrows waxed please."

My first thought. You cheeky bitch. But then, I thought of the money. What did I have to lose?

I turned up at his flat, armed with my wax strips. I lay him on my beauty couch and got to work on the bushes that housed his eyes.

Strip after strip, he yelped out in pain. I decided he wasn't worthy of my usual gentle touch. I was quite enjoying inflicting some pain on him.

"WHOOPS!" I suddenly screamed out. He shot up from the couch and looked straight in the mirror. He looked horrified as the realisation dawned on him that he had a rather large chunk missing from right in the middle of his brow.

Feigning complete innocence, I pulled the best sorry face that my Botox would allow.

"I'm so sorry. It was a complete accident."

Needless to say, he never made another appointment.

Chapter Forty-Two

It's not me it's them (Summer 2012)

To quote Tullene:
"You must be the unluckiest person I know when it comes to love and men."

I wouldn't disagree with her, nor would the rest of my friends and family. But her pearls of wisdom got me thinking. And before anyone says anything, yes, I am capable of getting the old grey matter to work. I'm very intellectual. I've got a degree, you know. A line I often pull out the bag if anyone questions my intellect.

But here I go, distracted and side tracked again. Back to what her pearls of wisdom got me thinking about. WHERE AM I GOING WRONG WITH MEN TO BE THIS UNDATE-ABLE?! So I thought, let me retrace my steps. After Jamie, I had two more potential Mr Rights who added themselves to my long list of Mr Wrongs.

Well, first up, there was a man from Chiswick. I met him on Grindr. And fuck me sideways, he actually wanted a date and not a quick bunk up on the high road. After the initial shock of being asked on a date (from Grindr), I accepted and we agreed to meet in a beautiful little pub on the river.

As soon as I saw him, I noticed he had slightly BFG ears but that didn't deter me. I thought how handy they would be to hold onto when he drops to his knees. PMA. Every cloud has a silver lining. The conversation was quite pleasant and the wine flowed like the rivers of Babylon. Until we got onto the topic of Boy Scouts. I disclosed that my cub leader had been arrested for fiddling with some of my fellow Cubs.

Yes, it's true. My cub leader was a paedophile. I had to be questioned by the cops when I was just an eight year old boy. Luckily, he was sent to prison.

As I continued on in this fashion of unsuitable date conversation, I felt Joan Rivers and Pam Ann (and Sauvignon Blanc) taking over my body and my mouth,

"I had to be questioned by the police. Luckily, he didn't touch me. I don't know why he didn't. I don't know what's wrong with me."

I sat there, laughing, and he looked at me,

"That's not funny!"

"Oh", my jaw dropped quicker than a gay boy in a football changing room. And before I knew it, he'd booked an Uber and left. Obviously didn't appreciate my sense of humour. Oh well, at least he'd said something and, for once, I had a reason for why a date had ditched me. Our senses of humour were definitely incompatible.

But as you know, you don't keep me down for long. Not unless it involves a rugby squad and blow jobs. Anyway, stop the side tracking. I'm scattier than a March hare. Is that even scatty? I don't know. I just remember my dear old Nan saying it from time to time. Oh no, it's just hit me. It's as mad as a March hare. Well, you get the drift!

Back to my story of the second Mr Wrong, who once again, came from Grindr. I know, you can see a pattern forming here, right? Well, we hit it off. We had a spark better than the New Year fireworks on the Thames. Or so I thought. We were up until 4 in the morning on our first couple of times talking. And then suddenly, nothing. He did a quicker U-turn than Theresa May. But I thought, hang on a damn second. I ain't having this. So I thought, for once, I'm going to get to the bottom of this behaviour.

So here is a transcript of a WhatsApp conversation:

MARK: I'm really interested to know what changed for you. Because we were talking till late at night, so full on and then nothing!

MR WRONG: I dunno. I just don't chase people and doubt we're compatible in the vanity sense, I don't care about Botox and fake tan.

MARK: But you knew about the fake tan and the Botox before you spoke to me.

MR WRONG: Well it didn't bother me but then it did. I can't help it, I'm just insecure with guys.

MARK: Well, if you'd have just given us a try, you might have had a great time. But now you'll just carry on with your insecurity. I was there, I was willing...

I do like having the last word. And I've never heard from either of these Grindr men ever again. Lesson one that I've learned, don't expect any more than a shag and an STD from Grindr. And lesson two, it's not always me, it's sometimes them. I felt so liberated.

Chapter Forty-Three

What a letdown (February 2013)

I will NEVER forget Len. I met him in a pub and we just clicked. I did notice that he kept going to the toilet during our date. I just assumed he had a weak bladder. And he seemed to sniff a lot. I just assumed he might be getting a cold.

Before I knew it, he'd taken me back to his place. No sooner had the front door shut behind us, Len lifted me up, kissing me passionately and carried me into the bedroom. He lifted his leg to slam the bedroom door shut behind us. And then threw me onto the bed. Very macho. I felt like Tanya Turner in *Footballers Wives*.

I already felt aroused so I pulled his trousers down and was presented with a VERY flaccid penis. How could he not have an erection? He read my thoughts.

"Sorry. I've been taking coke all night." Well, that killed the moment!

Chapter Forty-Four

A topless waiter and a piss-stained dancefloor (September 2013)

I was about to turn THIRTY and I decided I needed to organise a birthday bash to end all birthday bashes.

"What should the theme be?" I asked Tullene over a glass of Savvy B, "I want it to be classy."

"Tarts and vicars", she beamed.

I dropped her one of my death stares.

"I said classy. Not tacky."

Knocking back my New Zealand tipple, I had a lightbulb moment.

"HOLLYWOOD - glitz and glamour. That's the theme!" I declared. "Men in their penguin suits, women in their best frocks."

Theme confirmed, I set to work on organising the finer details. I wanted it to be the party of the century.

Fast forward a month and all my plans had come together. I arrived at the venue in a beautiful grey suit I had purchased especially for the occasion. I'd ensured I'd had a spray tan and, even though I said it myself, I looked as fit as fuck.

The first touch was a red carpet, leading all the way up the path to the front door. I felt like Joan Collins at the Oscars as I strolled along it. And then I clapped eyes on my topless waiter, Ivan. Yes, I'd ordered a topless beauty to hand out champagne to my guests as they turned up.

And fuck a duck, was he chiselled. The pecs were bigger than Pamela Anderson's tits, and he had nipples that could double as coat hooks. And don't get me started on the six pack that could grate cheddar.

Sipping on a glass of champagne that had been served to me by my hunk, the first guests started making their way into the party. Seeing the men in their suits and the women in glittery, posh gowns, I felt a lump in my throat. It was going to be a good night; I could feel it in my waters. And no, I wasn't coming down with a bladder infection. Nothing could possibly go wrong.

Everybody gasped as they strolled down the red carpet, surrounded by bubbles, which were coming from strategically placed machines. With the flood lights beaming down on the scene, it looked like a film premiere.

My guest's gasps for breath got even louder once they caught sight of the champagne being dished up to them by my topless God. Some of the perverts even copped a quick grope.

And as if red carpets and bubble machines weren't enough glamour, I even had a balloon arch for people to walk under as they entered. Now, call me egotistical but they spelt out MARK in big blue glittery balloons.

Once everyone had arrived, it was time to make my grand entrance. DJ cued and Ivan on my arm, he accompanied me up the red carpet whilst 'WOW' by Kylie Minogue blasted from the sound system. I was greeted with cheers and heckling as I made my official entry to my 30th year. Flashes blinded me as guests took multiple photographs. It felt like the press were there, papping away.

Making my way to the stage, Ivan kissed me on both cheeks as the DJ handed me a microphone.

"SPEECH! SPEECH!" The guests roared.

I went all coy.

"But I'm so shy", I gushed into the mic.

"BOLLOCKS!" I heard from my audience. They know me too well.

And as if by magic, a backing track to 'KISS KISS' by Holly Valance started to play. This is my signature tune. I know all the words and I'd decided I should treat them all to a song.

"When you look at me tell me what you see, this is what you get, it's the way I am..."

I belted out a verse and two choruses, quite tunefully if I do say so myself. And then the backing track started to skip and speed up. BIG HAIRY BALL SACKS.

Never one for being lost for words, I carried on, A cappella, like a true professional. The show must go on darlings. Bowing to rapturous applause, I bellowed down the microphone, Pink style, "Let's get the party started!"

And then a fireman walked in. SHIT. Where's the fire? My stomach turned. The room went silent as the dishy fireman approached and stopped right in front of me.

It was TRAVIS. My jaw dropped. Since when had he become a fireman?

"What are you doing here?"

"Mark?" He seemed equally confused.

"This is MY party", I informed him.

"Then I'm here for you."

I frowned. Well, that's a lie; I'd just had my Botox topped up for the occasion. But I definitely made the movement of a frown even if my face didn't oblige.

Travis handed a CD to the DJ and as the music began, the realisation dawned on me. Someone in this room had ordered me a stripper and Travis was it.

"You're a stripper?"

He nodded. Well, I had always wanted to see Travis naked, ever since I was a young boy at college all those years ago but I never dreamed it would turn out this way.

The crowd started yelping as he ripped his jacket off to reveal a stunning body. Travis gyrated up and down me like he was riding a fireman's pole and I couldn't resist having a quick stroke of his well formed torso..

And the way I was feeling right then, it's lucky that touching his body was the only kind of stroke I had. As he performed his stripping duties, I found myself gazing at him. I think it was that moment I realised I'd been in love with him ever since our fondle on my friend's bedroom floor.

Finally, down to his jock strap, which left little to the imagination, he was lapping up the attention of my party guests.

"OFF! OFF! OFF!"

And he obliged their cries. Before I could say fireman's lift, he'd whipped them off, thrown them into the air and they landed on my bonce. I'd be lying if I said I didn't have a quick sniff as I ripped them from my perfectly coiffed hair.

I looked down to catch a sneaky glance; I could do nothing but catch flies. I was looking at a python. Travis had a rather large penis. I didn't expect that, let me tell you.

I fanned myself as Travis put his clothes back on. A sweat had started to develop on my brow.

"It was nice to perform for you", he beamed at me as he was leaving the party.

"It was quite a shock", I assured him.

"Well. Bye then." Awkward silence.

"Won't you stay for a drink?" I bravely suggested.

"I can't. Got another party to get to."

"Getting your kit off for another poof?"

"Bet they won't be as good looking as you though."

And then the unbelievable happened. I think I actually turned a shade of crimson. Which is no mean feat considering I was covered in quite a thick layer of St. Tropez.

Travis leaned in and kissed me on the lips to say goodbye. It was a lingering kiss that felt like it went on for hours but I'm sure it didn't last more than a few seconds. I grabbed his hand as he went to make for the door.

"Don't go", I begged.

"I'm sorry Mark. But I have to."

And then he left. Bastard. I watched him as his fireman figure left a shadow on the red carpet.

"Someone's pissed on the dancefloor!" Jane broke my moment. Just as I gazed after the man I was in love with.

"What?"

"We need a mop. Before somebody breaks their neck!"

But it was too late. Before we had time to search, we heard a scream, followed by a CRASH, BANG, WALLOP! I looked over and saw it was Tullene, spread eagled. I gasped and ran towards her.

"TULLENE!" I looked down at her, in a heap. She'd gone arse over tit..

"I think I've broken my ankle", she yelled out in pain.

I glanced down at her legs, took a large gulp of Savvy B and screamed.

"Someone call a fucking ambulance!"

. . .

The mystery of the finger up the bum (October 2013)

Don't you just love a good wedding? I remember Tullene asking me to be her plus one at the marriage of two of her work colleagues. My first reaction was to say no. Me at any function Tullene invites me to is normally destined for doom.

"Is that bastard who called me a poof at your Christmas party going to be there?" That was my first question.

"No. He got the sack."

"I don't know Tullene. I won't know anyone."

And then Tullene pulled out her trump card.

"But I need someone to push me in my wheelchair."

Remember a few weeks before at my 30th birthday bash, Tullene had broken her ankle, and ever since, had been using it as emotional blackmail.

"If your friend hadn't pissed on the dancefloor, I wouldn't have slipped and ended up in the hospital."

Yes, it was all true. My 30th turned into quite a raucous affair and one of my friends, who shall remain nameless, became incontinent on the dancefloor. And before you could say, 'Tena Lady', Tullene had gone A over T and ended up being taken to A and E.

As the wedding was in Essex, the bride and groom arranged a coach to take everyone from London. Pushing Tullene up the ramp onto the bus, I wheeled her down the aisle and I suddenly realised the wheelchair wasn't moving. It was stuck between some seats.

Impatiently, the driver was tapping his steering wheel to indicate he was ready to leave. Tullene, her nervous laughter evoked, just sat there as I tried to dislodge the contraption she was lashed in.

"You're going to have to get out." I hissed through gritted teeth. Everyone's eyes were now on us and some rowdy boys began heckling.

"Get a move on!"

Said boys then got up from their seats and picked Tullene up in a fireman's lift, placing her in a seat. Crisis averted; the coach departed for Essex.

Arriving at the church, I demanded the same boys perform their heroic action once more and place her back in the wheelchair. Which they did, much to my best friend's delight.

"You and this fucking wheelchair!" I whispered in her ear as I pushed her up the gravel path towards God's house. Heaven help my parents when they get older and I have to become their carer.

As we made our way through the church door, I failed to see the small step that led down into the building. BANG! The wheelchair slipped from my grip and Tullene shot out like she'd been fired from a canon, her walking aid landing on top of the pile. Open mouthed, I looked down. Then up at the congregation. Then back down.

"OH MY GOD!" I screamed eventually and tried to look like I cared.

Hoping for no more wheelchair dramas, I tried to relax, and knocked back a large glass of Savvy B at the reception. I nearly choked on it however when I spotted an empty seat next to me.

"FUCK ME!" I bellowed, fearing Tullene had fallen out again without me noticing.

And then I looked up towards the dancefloor. I was greeted with Tullene, aided by a crutch, dancing like she'd been healed by the Lord. I marched up to her, steam escaping from my ears.

"You can bloody well walk for the rest of this trip!"

She stuck her finger up at me and swung her crutch above her head as she busted a move to 'Spinning Around' by Kylie. BITCH. Tullene, that is, not Kylie.

Sipping on another glass of Sauvignon at the bar, a beautiful man started chatting to me.

"Alex", he introduced himself, "I'm the groom's brother."

We flirted for the rest of the night and he forwardly invited himself up to my hotel room.

"I'm sharing with my best friend. That one with the supposed broken ankle. If you give me your number", I told him, "I'll text you once she's asleep and you can sneak in."

Once Tullene was fast asleep and snoring... Well, I say snoring. A lion's roar would be more apt with her nocturnal nose noises.

Alex sneaked into our hotel room and I dragged him on top of me in the bed. Yes, Tullene was next to us in the king size but, unlike her snoring, which could wake the dead, nothing wakes her.

A passionate night of love making began and it soon became clear that Alex had a penchant for the odd finger or two, up the you know where. Of course, I was more than happy to oblige. Myself and my fingers exhausted, Alex left me to fall asleep. Waking up in the morning, I stumbled to the bathroom, bleary eyed.

I heard Tullene roll over.

"I've got a really sore bum!" She shouted.

I gulped. And looked at my fingers.

"Oh god", were the only words I could spit out.

"It feels like someone's fingered it."

"Oh god." Was all I could say again.

And to this day, I pray that it was her piles playing her up and that I hadn't accidentally mistaken her bum for Alex's.

My H.I.V. scare (November 2013)

A few weeks after the wedding fiasco, I was still trying to

block out visions that I may have accidentally fingered Tullene's bum.

And I had been feeling unwell for a couple of weeks. As this was unlike me, Tullene was starting to get concerned.

"You need to see the doctor or go down the clap clinic", she insisted.

"But I haven't been a slut lately. The last bloke I slept with was that Alex at the wedding."

"It only takes one time!" I always hated it when Tullene was right.

I had been experiencing a fever and was constantly feeling tired. One night, I woke up with night sweats and I did the worse thing possible. I googled my symptoms.

H.I.V., I saw the letters staring back at me on my tablet. Shit.

The next morning, I phoned Tullene. She was taking no prisoners this particular day.

"Right, if you don't get yourself down to that clinic today, I'm going to drag you there myself."

I took no more convincing. I knew I needed to face it. Come what may. If I did have it, it was better to know and then I could deal with it.

I arrived at the STD department at St. Peter's hospital. Looking at the doors, I could have easily turned and run for my life. But I inhaled deeply and made my way through the revolving entrance.

Being taken into a room, I was confronted with a doctor. A big butch woman who made Mrs Trunchbull look like Mary Poppins.

"On the bed and strip!" She barked.

I went all meek.

"But I just want a blood test."

She was persistent and insistent that I get my kit off. So, I did as I was told and she performed a THOROUGH examination.

Sticking a swab up the eye of my penis was enough to ensure I never partook in unprotected sex ever again. It made my eyes water. And I'm not just talking about the ones on my face.

Embarrassing and intimate once over completed, she sat me down and I felt like I was being told off in the headmaster's office. I received a ten minute lecture on the virtues of safe sex.

"But my symptoms..." I wanted answers.

"Yes", she nodded, "it could well be H.I.V. BUT it might also be lots of other things."

Leaving the hospital, she told me I would get a phone call in a few days to tell me the results of my blood test. Now all I could do was wait.

As I exited the clap clinic, who should I spot? TRAVIS, walking along, hand in hand with a man.

"FUCK!" I internally screamed. Why here? Why now?

Seeing a van next to me, I quickly darted behind it and leant down, praying I hadn't been seen under the 'North Surrey GUM and Sexual Health Services' sign. But alas, it was too late.

"MARK!" I heard a voice call from behind me. Closing my eyes and breathing sharply out, I prayed there was someone else in the vicinity called Mark. Pretending I hadn't heard, I continued hiding behind the van.

But Travis was persistent.

"Mark! Can you hear me? I've got someone I want you to meet."

All of a sudden, Travis and the stranger were standing over me. I looked up from my gutter and forced my lips into the most convincing smile they could rummage. And all I could think about was Travis's massive penis. I knew it was there, underneath his trousers, looking down at me. A few moments of awkward silence ensued. I don't know why I didn't just stand up straight away but for some unknown reason, I stayed bent down.

"What are you doing down there?"

I searched for my best excuse.

"I lost an earring. I was just looking for it."

I saw Travis examine my ear lobe for a hole that didn't exist but he thought better of questioning me further. As I finally stood up, I saw Travis's eyes shoot up towards the GUM clinic sign. And then he looked back at me with the most suspicious look in his eyes. He chose not to mention it.

"This is Doug", he introduced us, "my fiancé."

Well, the unbelievable unhappened. I was lost for words.

"Nice to meet you", Doug said, holding out his hand. I shook it rather too enthusiastically. When all I really wanted to do was rip it off and slap Travis with it.

"Nice to meet you too", I spluttered. A complete lie. Inside, I had weird jealousy pangs. And all I could think was, "well, how on earth did you manage to get that bastard Travis to agree to marry you? I can't even get him to take me on a date." I felt deflated. I'd secretly always hoped that Travis might one day live up to his word and actually take me out. But alas, it obviously wasn't meant to be between us, especially as he was now engaged to be married.

"I hope his penis rips you in two." I don't know why I said it. It was supposed to be a thought. They both stood staring at me, open mouthed and I just spun on my heels and left them standing there.

Escaping Travis and Doug, I ran back to my car. Yes, I ran. I don't know why. Or how. And then I cried. Yes, I cried. And I don't know why I did that either.

Those days after my blood test were the longest days of my life. Three days later, I received a call from an unknown number.

"Hello?"

"This is Mary from North Surrey Gum and Sexual Health

services."

"Yes?"

"I'm pleased to tell you the result of your H.I.V. test is negative."

I cried again.

That time I went to India (February 2014)

I remember exactly where I was when Tullene phoned me and told me she wanted me to accompany her to India. I was happily minding my own business outside M&S in Barnes, the quiet leafy suburb in London. Well, it was quiet until I got this phone call. I mean, I screamed in shock. India had never been on my travel map wish list.

My instant answer was no. I'd heard horror stories about the dreaded Delhi belly. And as an IBS sufferer, I didn't quite think this was the ideal holiday destination for one who already has a weak stomach constitution. And secondly, being gay in India was still illegal so that thought made me shit my little gay IBS pants.

But as everyone who knows me would say, I am spontaneous and like to grab life by the balls (pun intended). I gave Tullene a very big YES answer. You only live once. I should go, even at the risk of getting the shits and being arrested for being a sausage smuggler.

And I am quite partial to an Indian. And I'm not just talking about a curry.

We boarded our Virgin Dreamliner (only the best darlings). As you know, my friends often call me a pharmacy. I have a pill for every occasion or eventuality. I checked each one off. Paracetamol. Pepto Bismol. Imodium. Mosquito repellent. Multibionta. Dioralyte. Anti-sickness pills. Lucozade.

Our Dreamliner touched down and my stomach was turning

quicker than a washing machine's spin cycle. It was my first trip abroad where I was genuinely nervous. We stepped outside the airport doors and we breathed in the air. And soon wished we hadn't. The air down a sewer would have been fresher.

As we waited for our taxi, a man picked up our luggage. Oh, how friendly. Helping us like this. He put them on top of the taxi for us and our driver strapped them to the roof. With a piece of rope that I could have used as dental floss. I took a deep breath (forgetting about the lack of fresh air) and prayed our luggage would make it.

Now, for anyone who's not ventured to India. Let me give you some advice. Don't be fooled by these lovely men who help you with your luggage. Because as I went to shut the taxi door, the fake porter grabbed the door and started demanding money. I tell you, it's lucky I've built up the muscles in my wrists over the years. As it meant I won the battle of the taxi door. I managed to pull it shut and told the driver to pedal it!

Does anyone else love the taxi drive from the airport to your hotel? I love the opportunity to take in the sights. Little did we realise the driving standards and speed of India. It's impossible to take in the sights. I'm telling you now, people swerve in and out of traffic, beeping their horns. Tullene and I held on for dear life and the only sight I managed to take in was Tullene's armpit.

I'd never been so happy to see a red traffic light in my life, as it meant we had a little respite from the lunacy of the roads. That was until a Hijra woman stuck her hand through the taxi window, begging for money.

Anyone who knows me and Tullene will know our habit of laughing when we get nervous or scared. Which was exactly our reaction to this predicament. Obviously, she thought we were mocking her and reached for my spiky hair which she managed to grip. Well, that sure stopped us laughing...

Using Grindr in India (February 2014)

I was just about to be scalped by this Hijra woman who thought we were taking the piss. And as if a prayer had been answered, the traffic light turned green and off we zoomed. I breathed a sigh of relief when we finally arrived at our hotel.

HOTEL HELLHOLE. I sincerely recommend that any visitors to Delhi avoid this establishment at all costs. It makes Sainsbury's Basics look like the M&S Best of British range.

As we stepped out of the taxi, (yes, our luggage was still strapped to the roof, thank God), we were greeted by a couple of prostitutes. What a desirable neighbourhood. Tullene started panicking and I thought I was going to have to give her a slap.

We were escorted to our room and as I stepped inside, I just wanted to step back outside. The curtains were yellow, and the bedding... Well, I can't even do justice to the bedding by using any English language.

Desperate for a wee, I strolled into the bathroom and was greeted by a bucket.

"We've got to get out of here!" I screamed.

Little did I know that Tullene was already outside the door, luggage in hand with the same thought. We checked out of Aura and put ourselves in a tuk tuk.

"Get us to the nearest IBIS!" We demanded.

If you ever venture to India, there is no other way to travel than a tuk tuk. But I advise you to cling on for dear life. And to say your prayers because they certainly know how to dodge in and out of traffic. In fact, I think a tuk tuk journey is the perfect cure for constipation, should you have that problem.

After every journey in India, whether it be by car, tuk tuk or even walking, I looked up to the sky and thanked the Lord that I'd survived.

Finally, in an IBIS, we felt safe. And we had WIFI. I was

desperate to get on Grindr. I must confess, I thought they wouldn't have this app in India because of the fact being gay was illegal.

But I was blown away, (pardon the pun). In the space of being logged in for five minutes, I had twenty messages. I'm telling you now, my iPhone nearly crashed. My Grindr was pinging off the hook.

I was being sent picture after picture of the local talent... topless talent and talented cock. I was dripping faster than a Mr. Whippy in Madrid. In my element, I was. I was like Harry Potter in a wand shop.

I got excited. But then it suddenly hit me like a wet kipper.

It's illegal in this country, so I bottled it.

And then one really caught my eye. A very attractive guy, who was staying at our hotel. Not far to go then. I got excited. But then I gave myself another reality check. I can't be locked up in an Indian jail, being made to pick up the soap. I'd be the prison bitch.

Mmm, what a fantasy. Maybe I should get myself arrested.

And then I came down to earth with a bump. The guy who I'd blown out (not literally) had sent me a message in Punjabi. Does he realise I'm English and not bilingual? Thank God for google translate. My eyes widened as Google told me that he'd called me a gay bitch. What a cunt!!

I switched Grindr off for the night. It was starting to get on my moobs. Tullene was already heavily snoring so I rolled over to go to sleep and I heard rustling coming from the suitcase.

"Tullene! Wake up. There's a cobra in the suitcase!"

Visiting the Taj Mahal (February 2014)

As you have probably guessed by the fact I'm still writing about our Indian adventure, Tullene and I survived the cobra in the suitcase. Well, I say Cobra, it was actually a piece of poly-thene rustling under the air conditioning.

Now, no visit to India would be complete without a trip to the Taj Mahal. So, off we went in our private hire car, complete with our own driver. Only the best for us.

As we set off, I was reminded once more of the very bumpy roads. Clearly, no one pays road tax in India. Or if they do, the government certainly doesn't spend the money on improving roads. The number of times my head bounced off the roof, I'm surprised I didn't get a concussion.

After being constantly violated by the seat belt holder migrating up my bum, we finally arrived at the Taj Mahal. I am rarely rendered speechless, but on this occasion, I had no words. It's one of the most beautiful sights I have ever witnessed in my entire life; I even had tears in my eyes. Another rare occurrence. I'm often called a stone-hearted gay boy.

As you'd expect, security is very high as you enter the grounds of the Taj Mahal. I had to have my man bag searched. Even though I've got nothing to hide, any security always makes me so nervous. I have an irrational fear that someone may have planted drugs on me and I'll be locked up in jail.

My bag came out the other side of the X-ray machine and I saw three security guards grab my bag. Oh shit, I thought, some-one, has planted drugs in my man bag. I felt sweat drip and hit my HD eyebrows.

They ripped open my man bag and pulled out my Gay Times magazine.

"You can't have this!" I heard the security guard bellow. And he turned around and ripped it up. Bloody cheek. I was more annoyed that I hadn't even read that issue yet.

After that nerve-wracking incident, I decided I needed to urinate. I found some toilets (not the best or cleanest facilities I've ever whipped my cock out in, but they had to do). As I stood peeing at the urinal, I noticed an arm, rubbing against my arm.

I plucked up the courage to look across and I witnessed this man, staring down at my penis. Cor, he's got no shame. It's clearly a novelty to see a spray tanned British cock.

We entered the grounds and saw some wild monkeys. That was a sight I just had to capture. I got my camera and started papping the monkeys. The next thing I knew, we were surrounded and circled by ten monkeys, all nipping at our ankles. I don't think they appreciated having their photo taken.

All that was going through my mind was the fact I hadn't had a rabies jab. When my pharmacist asked me if I'd be in contact with wild monkeys, I'd said, 'oh no, of course not'.

Famous last words.

Finally, being rescued by the monkey whisperer, we went down to the souvenir stalls outside the Taj Mahal. But shopping in India really annoyed me. No one just lets you browse. They're always trying to sell you things. Got right on my man tits. As we were walking along this particular market, a man grabbed my arm and dragged me inside his shop. Jesus, I screamed, this is forceful selling.

"Why don't you get rid of your friends and come into my stock room with me?"

Obviously, doesn't want to sell me any material items, I thought. My eyes widened at his question and I did consider it for a moment. He was rather attractive and you know my partiality to an Indian man.

Even though being gay is illegal in India, they're all at it. Not afraid of the law clearly. I had to decline as Tullene was waiting for me outside. But he was so attractive, I had to drag myself away.

In conclusion, I decided, I'm clearly not undateable in India…. Maybe I should move???

Chapter Forty-Five

Going for a ride (May 2014)

Now I know dear readers that you will automatically assume that I am talking about sex. But I'm actually talking about the innocent act of riding a bike. And before any smart arses ask what bike riding has got to do with dating, let me fill you in. Pun intended.

I'd been loosely seeing a lovely man from Chichester, the odd date here and there, the occasional stroll along the harbour, the rare fornication or three.

Just before Easter, this said man invited me on a mini break to West Wittering in West Sussex. To quote Bridget Jones, "a mini break, it must be true love!" I was so excited; I'd never been whisked away on a mini break before. I was getting butterflies inside, certain that this was the man for me.

And for those of you who know West Wittering, and the surrounding areas, will know what a beautiful part of our country it is. My absolute favourite place in the whole wide world!

I made the suggestion that we go for a bike ride on our first day. I could think of nothing more exciting or romantic than riding along together, through country lanes and down sand dunes, with the wind rushing through our hair, staring into each other's eyes over the handlebars.

Now the only issue I had was my car. For those close to me will know that my car is the size of a Smart car, so there was no way my bike was fitting in that. But my dear Father came up with the solution. I could borrow his fold-up bike. I said yes, but that was before I'd clapped eyes on it. What a god-awful contraption. It had to be seen to be believed.

Day one and the sun was shining down on us in West Sussex. To quote my dear Nan, the sun always shines on the righteous, so I felt optimistic.

After Chichester man had contained his fit of the giggles at the sight of my Father's fold-up bike, we set off for our ride like a scene from Gone with the Wind.

As the wind tickled my ever-balding scalp, I turned to look back at my riding companion. Joy filled my heart along with the ripe sea air filling my lungs. God, I sound like I'm writing a sickening romance novel.

We'd ridden about two miles when we arrived in Bracklesham Bay and I noticed a lady walking along with a pram. Chichester man had now overtaken me and was a few hundred yards ahead. He seemed to be much faster than me as you could hardly gather much speed on my Father's archaic, fold up, contraption.

In the silence of the country lanes, I suddenly heard a loud snapping sound which echoed down the street. Even the lady with the pram heard it and we shared eye contact as the confusion on our face was mutual. As I fell backwards from the bike, it soon became clear that the snap was the saddle. And the next thing I knew, I was on my back in the gutter, legs akimbo with a saddle on top of me and a bike slumped in the kerb.

I let out an almighty shriek as I went down like a sack of shit.

It was so loud; it could be heard on the Isle of Wight. People gathered around me and all I could see were faces staring down at me. After the circle of faces realised nothing more than my pride was hurt, they dispersed and carried on about their business. I stood up, bike in one hand, saddle in the other. Chichester man was nowhere to be seen. Had he not seen what had happened to me? Had he not realised I was no longer riding along behind him? Or had he felt too embarrassed to acknowledge he was with the saddle snapping gay boy? I would just like to take this opportunity to point out that the bike's weight limit is 15 stone and I am only 12 stone, 11 pounds.

Realising my mini-break companion had done a Houdini on me, I decided to walk back and find the nearest pub. I needed a pint. As I strolled into the pub with the saddle in my hand, a man looked at me most peculiarly.

"That's a funny looking bike!" he dared to remark. To which I snapped back,

"Don't even talk to me about this fucking bike!" Poor man. I bet he wished he'd never commented.

The moral of the story. Never ride a fold up bike. And never assume a mini-break means true love.

Chapter Forty-Six

That time I went to prison (July 2014)

When I was first invited to visit a male prison to do an interactive social group with the LGBT community inside, I shit myself and nearly didn't commit to the project.

What the fuck was I going to talk about? Yes, I grew up on quite a rough council estate where crime was high but luckily, I'd avoided prison, unlike many of the boys I grew up with.

The closest I'd ever been on the wrong side of the law was that time I got thrown into the police cells at Brighton nick for being drunk and disorderly.

As I pulled up at the prison, it was very daunting. There was this massive building in front of my eyes, surrounded by barbed wire. It was lucky I'd taken a couple of Imodium that morning, let me tell you.

I was given a tour when I first arrived and it's very surprising how much it actually looked like the Bad Girls set. I was scared of bumping into any real-life prisoners. I wasn't sure what the rough, macho, non-gay ones would make of this mincing homo.

As 2 pm came closer, it was time for me to be escorted to the chapel to begin my LGBT group with the gay prisoners. Yes, it was being held in the chapel. The irony wasn't lost on me.

As I was being taken into the chapel, an officer stopped me at the main doors and asked for my name. I obligingly gave it and she announced I wasn't on the list so I couldn't gain entry.

Looking very confused, another officer came to my rescue.

"He's not a prisoner. He's the guest speaker!"

Realising her mistake, she let me through but I couldn't help blurting out, "Do I look like a prisoner?"

I sat down in the chapel after I'd organised the chairs into a circle, a la Alcoholics Anonymous style. My only other option was a straight line and that was far too formal for my liking.

Sweaty palms and heart palpitations, I saw the big hand heading towards the 2. I didn't know what to expect. I'd been told I had a man who murdered his husband and an arsonist, among others.

As they entered, my butterflies escaped through the bars. The husband killer came in and shook my hand, whilst hugging me and kissing me on the cheek. The rest made similar entrances and greetings and automatically put me at ease.

I'd been far too focused on the fact that I was in a prison and forgotten that in reality, I was just talking to fellow human beings who also happen to be gay. And just so happen to have made mistakes.

Each person had their own individuality and within seconds, I'd forgotten I was even inside a prison. We talked, we laughed and we discussed sex. A LOT.

After an hour, a prison buffet was bought into the room for us. It looked bloody delicious. Even though I must confess I was a little wary of eating it after being told it had been prepared by the prisoners in the prison kitchen.

One of the gay prisoners, Mike, who I took quite a shine to (and he to me), assured me that as long as I wasn't a paedophile, the food was quite safe to eat. I told him I was guilty of many things, but that wasn't one of them.

Whilst shoving a prison-issued cheese roll into my gob, a big Zimbabwean prisoner came and grabbed me by the arm,

"You look so good! My cell number is 427 if you want to come back later!"

I nearly choked on my cheese roll and managed to choke out the words,

"I think you'd split me in two!" which was met with roars of laughter from the whole group. His tight grey jogging bottoms left little to the imagination and it was clear to see he was MORE than well endowed.

They talked about their lives and it left me feeling rather humbled. Yes, I got bullied at school for being gay but on the whole, I've been widely accepted by my family and friends. But some of these men have been abandoned by their families for being homosexual. One of the men was even imprisoned in Russia for attending a gay pride event. It certainly opened my eyes.

I think it was refreshing for them to be a part of this social group and be able to freely express themselves and their sexuality without any fear.

Before I was leaving, the prisoners were begging me to go back. They loved our afternoon and it went on much longer than I expected.

After three hours, the officers were having to chuck me out because we had gone on for far too long and I was putting out the schedules. But it was honestly one of the best experiences of my life. Actually, doing a random act, something worthwhile on the front line, from one gay boy to my fellow LGBT community, was much better than any money I've ever raised for charity.

My final words were from Mike.

"I get out in seven weeks. How can I contact you?"

I quite fancied him. He was just my type so it would have been rude to discriminate against him just because he's in prison. So, I made sure to tell him how to contact me.

Chapter Forty-Seven

My 'Almost' Happy Ending with a Transgender (August 2014)

After falling in love with a prisoner, I'd deleted all my dating apps. There wasn't one to be found on my iPhone. I was fed up with all the curious straight men chatting to me on Plenty of Fish. And annoyed at everybody on Grindr for being shallow and only wanting one thing. And don't even get me started on Tinder.

I may have only been in my 30s but I'm rather Granny-like when it comes to technology. After an unfortunate incident involving a 70-year-old lady and swiping right, and then being slightly stalked and receiving numerous invites for coffee and cake, I'd decided that Tinder was no good for me either.

I've taken to more intellectual apps these days. My favourite is Words with Friends. For those of you not in the know, this is Scrabble. But on your phone. And you can play with anyone, anywhere in the world.

One day, I started playing with this very handsome man called Joshua. Yes, you get to see a photo of who you're playing with. I kept perving on his picture whilst waiting for him to play his move, praying he would start a conversation.

And then the Lord answered my prayers and a chat popped up. Although it was a little ambiguous. Remember, this is not a gay app, so there's no way of knowing whether the person you're playing with fancies you. Or even if they're a raving homo.

After putting my journalistic training into practice, it was soon confirmed that Joshua was flirting with me and did indeed fancy me.

He was only 21. Ten years younger than me but I decided that I could be a cougar if I wanted. And he lived in Southampton. I was a bit disappointed that he wasn't in London but hey-ho, it's only an hour's drive or a train ride away! And besides, I've become so institutionalised with being single, I thought it'd be perfect to have a man who didn't live in my pocket.

We spent months talking on the phone, exchanging WhatsApp messages and sending each other photos. I don't think I've ever fancied a man as much as I had Joshua.

He was just my type; Tattoos, quite butch, and BLOODY handsome.

We had so much in common. We drank like fishes. We had potty mouths and both adored the C U Next Tuesday word. And we both had quite common, rough around the edges, accents. Surely it was a match made in heaven.

We even discussed growing older together. And I'd never met another man who shared the same views as me about how we should behave in a care home as an old couple together. We both agreed that it would be wheelchair races through the corridors. And slipping under the table for a sly blowjob during bingo.

A few months of a long-distance telephone relationship, I decided it was finally time to bite the bullet. Being the older gentleman, I took the lead and arranged to get the train from

London to Southampton. I was finally going to meet the man of my dreams, my perfect match.

Two days before the big first date, he sent me a message declaring, "We're perfect for each other, I swear." I swooned at the words and I was of the same opinion. We were so similar, the way we spoke, the thoughts we had. It was scary.

The night before I was due to catch my train to Southampton, we had a very interesting text conversation.

JOSHUA: Probably something I should tell you before you come in case it puts you off.

ME: What??

JOSHUA: I'm transgender. I was born a female. I know you'll probably freak and it's fine.

MARK: I don't give a shit. I know you as Joshua and I fancy you.

The morning of the date arrived and the sun was shining so brightly

I arrived at Southampton Docks in plenty of time for our meeting. We'd agreed on 1 pm. It got to ten past and no sign of him. I tried to call. No answer. It got to twenty past. I sent two messages. No reply.

As the clock hit 2 pm, I thought, What a C U Next Tuesday. I've come all the way from London and you don't even have the common human decency to show up or even respond to my attempts at contact.

Being ever the positive boy that I am, I decided that I would not waste my day. The sun was beating down and, it was the most beautiful day, so I spent my unexpected free time wandering around Southampton. I had a few glasses of wine, ate a spot of lunch and watched the world go by.

A few glasses of savvy b later, I decided it was time to get the train back to London. But not before I sent one final message to Joshua. I simply had to have the final word:

"I had a lovely day in the sun at Southampton Docks. I thought it best not to waste the train tickets so I spent the day in Southampton anyway. I wouldn't worry what people think of you because you're transgender. I'd be more concerned with what people think of you because you're a bit of a cunt."

Chapter Forty-Eight

Joining a gay walking group (September 2014)

For years, my friends had been nagging me to get some gay friends. Apparently, they're concerned that my circle consists of straight ladies, their husbands, and my gaggle of old dears from the church. Well, they are correct.

"You'll never find a life partner surrounded by us!" Are they trying to tell me something? Lucky I'm not a sensitive soul otherwise I might have thought they were trying to palm me off.

In a way, I guess they were right. Being stuck in my circle of 'straights' is probably not the most pro-active approach to meeting 'the one', or any gay friends come to that.

After their persistent advice, I finally decided to take action. I Googled gay men's groups. And up popped a gay man's dinner club. I quickly searched for the date of the next meal, only to discover the group was now defunct.

Probably for the best. I'm sure it would have ended up involving copious amounts of alcohol and I'd have bedded half the men before you could say 'what's on the menu tonight?'

Known for my perseverance, I refused to give up at the first hurdle. As I scoured the Google search engine, the Gay Outdoor Club caught my eye.

Once I'd clarified that it wasn't a dogging event, I became increasingly disinterested. JOKE. I became very interested.

I soon discovered that it was a gay walking group. How exciting. Not only would I get to meet fellow gays, I would get exercise and fresh air into the bargain. I had two options to choose from. A London group or the Surrey Hills. Coming to the conclusion that I could walk around London anytime, I decided on the Surrey Hills.

I also noticed that they indulge in coffee and cake at the end of each walk. Cute. And the cakes are baked by some of the members. Being an amateur Mary Berry myself, this gave my spatula a twinge of excitement.

Armed with a lemon drizzle loaf (my speciality), I nervously turned up at my first walk. This particular day was a 13-mile ramble around Hascombe. Yes, Hascombe. I still don't bloody know where it is but it's blooming beautiful.

Shaking hands with all the men that were attending the walk was daunting and as the introductions finished, it was clear that I brought the median age range down by about twenty years.

One of the older guys came up to me and offered me a sweet from an open bag he had in his hand. Ignoring advice I'd been given as a child about accepting sweets from strangers, my hand reached into his sweetie bag.

"Which colour willy would you like?" He bellowed as my fingers realised they were fiddling with sugar-laden penises.

As we set off on our walk, the usual small talk ensued as I was asked, "Where do you live?" "What's your job?" But it was so bloody nice. The surroundings were glorious and I was engaging in conversation with some really friendly people. And they were gay. My friends would be so proud of me. The only conversations I've had with gay men in recent years have been via Grindr.

A few miles in and this rather charming, camp, man called Robert came up to me and grabbed me by the arm. Maybe this is a dogging group after all, I thought as I felt his hand on my arm.

"I just have to tell you darling. Your eyebrows are FABU-LOUS! They are even better than Kim Kardashian's!"

We soon spent the rest of the afternoon laughing and talking random rubbish with each other. We had the same stupid sense of humour and outrageous outlook on life.

As I left the walk that day, my eyebrow admirer came running up to kiss me goodbye. "I feel like I've known you my whole life!" He said as we embraced. And it was true. We had clicked automatically. And do you know what was even more refreshing? It was a purely platonic encounter. I certainly felt no romantic notion towards him and I knew the feeling was mutual.

As the walks are only once a month, I found myself counting down the days until the next one. I've now been a member for five years and love every minute of the days out.

It's so amazing seeing parts of the countryside that I would never, ever venture into. And with wonderful conversation and laughs from many beautiful souls I've met. It's innuendo city most of the time. Which is right up my alley. Pardon the pun.

It's the best decision I've made in years to join. My advice to you all: Even if you feel scared, just take the plunge. Join that group, book that trip. Grab life by the balls!

During the most recent walk, I engaged in conversation with the chairman.

"We are always looking for new people to lead the walks", he told me.

"I'd bloody get us lost!" I insisted.

"That's what I thought five years ago and look at me now. I lead walks and I'm the chairman!"

"Are you trying to groom me?" I quickly retorted. Oh, how we laughed.

Jokes aside, Tullene later said to me that she can see me becoming the chairman one day. Watch this space!

Chapter Forty-Nine

Downloading Plenty of Fish (Nearly every Christmas period but this particular time-Boxing Day 2014)

T do it every Christmas period. For some unbeknown reason, usually around Boxing Day, I decide it might be a good idea to go in search of a husband. I don't know what comes over me. It must be the excessive plonk consumed over the festive period.

Or, on a more serious note, it could be the fact that Christmas makes me feel all loved up and warm and fuzzy inside. And gives me the notion that it might actually be nice to fall in love after all.

Although I must confess, I've forgotten what it's like to be in requited love. Without wanting anybody to crack out the violins, it has been more years than I care to remember.

So, there I was on this one particular Boxing Day night, staring at the present-less Christmas tree, clutching a bottle of Single Malt Scotch Whisky. Yes, I know it's rare for anything other than New Zealand Savvy B to pass my lips, but I do like to treat myself from time to time.

After my third large Scotch, I stood up determinedly and

declared to myself that I would find a husband. Dramatically pressing the buttons on my iPhone, I downloaded Plenty of Fish.

Obviously, I picked my best photographs and kept my profile simple.

"Love to laugh, love to have fun. Love the theatre, the beach, swimming, reading and writing. And I love men!"

Within minutes, a lovely looking chap called Matthew popped up in my inbox. Yes, I know, I just used the word CHAP. I'm clearly getting old. I even used the word DISCO when describing a CLUB the other day.

Anyway, back to Matthew who seemed rather forward.

"Let's video chat", he insisted.

Okay, I thought. At least I'll get to see him in the flesh and it will give me a glimpse of his true personality. It's so easy to hide behind a keyboard.

As I pressed accept on the video chat, I saw that he was topless. I was in a two-piece pyjama set but each to their own.

The call started off with small talk and then he panned down his pecs and six-pack. What a body, I thought to myself.

And then he came to his piece de resistance. I saw him clutching his fully erect manhood, rather seductively. Now, I'm no prude but in my naivety, I truly believed this video call was to be an initial test to judge our compatibility.

"Watch me wank!" He bellowed through the iPhone screen at me.

Being the ever-accommodating gay boy, I obliged. But after his voyeurism, I never heard from Matthew again and I noticed that he'd blocked me. Bastard.

Never mind, an extremely cute bloke called Louie popped up into my inbox to distract my attention away from being dumped by Matthew.

. . .

Within seconds, I noticed that Louie was probably not looking for a relationship. His profile classed him as straight and looking for a woman. What is it with Plenty of Fish and straight men chasing the homos?

Well, Louie was beautiful and willing, so who was I to turn down a chat, gay or not? He started the proceedings.

"Do you want me to wank for you Sir? I'm so horny Daddy. Can I call you Daddy?"

Being an ex-holiday park entertainer, I'm not one to turn down the chance to partake in performing arts.

"Yes, you can call me Daddy. And you better respect me", I typed sniggering.

"Okay. Tell me what you want me to do Master Daddy."

In the meantime, I saw another supposedly straight man arrive in my inbox. Terry. He wanted me to make a video for him. And he was certainly precise in his direction. Eat your heart out Stephen Spielberg.

.   .   .

"Have your legs over your shoulders with your wet fingers running over your juicy hole."

Not being an acrobat, I feared I may have had a problem in obliging. And being a writer, I'm not opposed to engaging in a bit of naughty talk. But I draw the line at dirty videos. You never know when they might come back to bite you on the bum. Pun absolutely intended.

That time, I took a leaf out of Matthew's book and made use of the block feature of the app.

And then, just as I was about to give up, my fortunes changed. An 'actual' gay man sent me a message. Darrel. And he asked for no dirty talk or sexually explicit videos. He engaged in purely decent conversation, obviously on a quest to find love.

We spent a few days sending endless messages to each other. It was going so well. We'd even started to arrange a first date.

He happened to ask me what I'm giving up for New Year. I informed him that I'm giving up swearing.

"Is your swearing really that bad?" He asked me.

"I'd be lying if I said the C U Next Tuesday word doesn't often leave my lips. Back off now if you're easily offended."

And, with that, Darrel showed me that he's also capable of making use of the block button.

What a C...

Chapter Fifty

The One that got away; Part One (April 2015)

I have a massive love for the theatre. Even bigger than my love for the male species. I go to see a show at least two or three times a month. A musical. A comedy. A play. Whatever I can feast my eyes on. I adore it all.

There was this one night back in April 2015 and I was taking my sister, Clare, out to see a play. Yes, I had forgiven her by now after she outed me to my parents.

It was a comedy called 'Dirty Dusting.' All about three old ladies who are cleaners but, when they realise they don't have enough money to pay their bills, they start their own sex chatline. It was completely hilarious. If you ever see it advertised, I advise you to get your arse down to where it's playing and see it.

This particular night it was on at the Beck theatre in Hayes. Not the most desirable place but if you drive through the town with all your car doors locked, you might just survive.

A glass of cold Savvy B in my hand - Yes, I was shocked too that a theatre in Hayes had a New Zealand wine on the menu, but there you go - and we settled down in the front row. YES, the front row. My friends call me a theatre snob, but I make no apologies, if I'm going to see something, I want the best view. And this particular night, it turned out to be well worth it.

Amongst this all-female cast was a rather dashing man playing the boss of the cleaning company. Being in the front row, I had a very good view of the merchandise and it was certainly worth ogling over. I had to meticulously place my glass of Savvy B on my crotch to stop my sister getting any nasty surprises in her peripheral.

During the interval, my sister had told me she'd noticed me eyeing up this handsome actor and made it her mission to make me red faced about the whole affair.

"We should wait backstage after the performance. You can chat him up!" She insisted.

"Oh no. I couldn't!" I retorted, unnaturally bashful.

"He was DEFINITELY looking straight at you every time he came on!"

I daren't tell her that I nearly came every time he DID too!

As the curtain closed on the final act, I ensured I drew as much attention to myself as possible. When my future husband, whoops, slip of the keyboard, I meant, when this actor came on to take his bow, I stood up and gave an awfully loud applause and a wolf whistle.

Unfortunately, I've never mastered the art of wolf whistling. And so my attempt turned into an impression of a baby blowing a raspberry. Right in front of my eyes, and his, we saw my spit land at his feet.

Mortified, I threw myself back down in my seat and quickly flipped open the programme, pretending I was engrossed in the blurb. I didn't dare look up as the cast exited stage left. Actually, as I wasn't looking at the time, I've no idea which exit they took.

Clare grabbed my hand and tried her hardest to drag me to

the stage door. But the Virgo in me dug my heels in and I barked at her to get her short arse to the car. My sister is vertically challenged. Coming in at four foot ten, she is one inch from being classified as a dwarf.

Clare was still stood by the stage door as I started the car engine. I put my Peugeot into gear and revved hard. When she saw I was serious and would indeed drive off without her, she soon thought better of it and ran towards the motor. I think it suddenly dawned on her that she was in Hayes.

Home, I flopped myself onto my faux leather sofa and poured another large glass of my favourite tipple. It was drowning my sorrows time after letting this actor get away, whom, I had found out, was called Liam. I could be a private detective. Either that or I'm just very good at reading theatre programmes.

Feeling a little squiffy, that's another word for tipsy, I decided to use my new found detective skills and partake in a bit of Twitter stalking. Before you could say 'bunny boiler', I found Liam and tweeted him:

"Having a hoover down your Y fronts and coming onto the stage in gold hot pants made our night. Great show. Loved it!"

The tweet had the desired effect. Within minutes, Liam had sent me a private message and then we talked for hours that night.

I discovered that he came from Newcastle and was just in London on tour with the show.

This deflated me a little as I've so often seen long distance relationships fail. But I soon adopted my PMA mantra and decided that a small thing like distance wouldn't be a barrier. Before I knew it, we were Facetiming every night before bed.

Chapter Fifty-One

The one that got away; Part Two (May 2015)

We enjoyed a month of nightly FaceTime, which often involved my Mum joining in. Yes, she doesn't like to miss out on anything. One warm night in May, we finally decided that now was the time to bite the bullet.

He was going to get the train down from Newcastle to visit me in London. As I was still living with my parents at the time, I thought it best to book a beautiful little hotel. I didn't think our first time together would be awfully romantic under my parent's roof. Even though I was now over 30, my devout Catholic Mother would still not allow me to share a bed with a boyfriend. Not unless I married them first.

And since we'd only seen each other in the flesh once, me as an audience member and he as an actor performing to said audience, I thought it a little premature to be throwing around any marriage proposals.

I don't mind telling you, on the day he was due to arrive at Victoria, I had butterflies. And I feel an overshare coming on, but

I'd hardly spent two minutes away from the latrine that morning. Raiding my Mum's medicine cabinet, I dosed up on Imodium.

Now, for anybody who knows me personally, will know that I am not renowned for my fashion sense. I opted for a pair of jeans, a t-shirt and a cardigan. I personally thought I looked fit but as I was leaving to walk out the door, my mother grabbed my arm.

"Are you sure that's the best choice of outfit?" An awkward silence ensued between us and I pursed my lips in her direction. I did raise my eyebrows too, but she couldn't tell.

Looking my mum up and down, the irony of her being dressed in just a petticoat and bra as she dished out the fashion advice, wasn't lost on me. Deciding that headbutting one's mother is not the most Christianly action to partake in, I chose to ignore her.

"He shall have to take me as I am mother! Or not at all!" And I flounced out the door.

Waiting at Victoria station, my stomach in training for the 2016 Olympics, I was glad I'd taken a butt blocker, as my father calls them.

Liam stepped onto the platform and he was even more beautiful than I had remembered. His blue eyes dazzled in the sunlight as he approached me. I can't be sure if it was sunny this particular morning but that line sounds better if we pretend it was.

Having become acquainted on FaceTime and the telephone, I felt like we had known each other for years. I don't know what came over me but I suddenly burst into my best impression of Julie Andrews in 'The Sound of Music.' Running towards him, wind rushing through my hair. Yes, I hadn't gone bald yet.

As we reached each other after our slow-motion approach, I flung my arms around him and rested my head on his chest. No, not because I'm a pervert and have a nipples fetish (which I am and which I do), but because he was so bloody tall.

A nice tall man. My eyes lit up. Tall man, long....

Trousers. Take your minds out the gutter.

We walked along the platform, hand in hand. I don't know what Liam had done to me as, even to this day, I'm not one for PDA'S. (Public Displays of Affection) But it just felt right to hold this man's hand.

First stop was tea and cakes with Mother Morgan. She insisted she be the first to meet him, else I would be written out of her will. Oh, the blackmail. I promise you. She is a devout catholic indeed.

As we walked up the garden path, towards my parent's patio door, my mum made it no secret that she was twitching the curtains to get a good glimpse. But I could see she was instantly impressed.

Liam was dressed in a suit. I kid you not, a suit! Talk about showing me up. I looked like a chav, turning up to Aldi to do the weekly shoplifting, in comparison.

Liam embraced my mother and kissed her on both cheeks. Very continental.

"Lovely to meet you Mrs Morgan."

My mother's eyes filled up with fresh tears of joy, as she looked Liam up and down. And then she did the same to me. Except the tears turned to disdain.

"I told him to change his outfit Liam. But do you think he would listen?"

The act of headbutting had started to seem more appealing.

It was lunchtime after the mother's meeting, so I suggested we stop at Budgens to grab a bite to eat. My dear friend Lynne still works there and she always makes me the most delicious bacon roll with cheese and BBQ sauce. I'll let you debate my choice of cuisine independently.

As Lynne saw us glide along the aisle towards her, (I'm not sure we did glide - after all, we're not Torvill and Dean - but it sounds romantic), her eyes beamed like a lighthouse on the Isle of Wight coastline.

"Liam. This is Lynne. We call her the Welsh windbag." Very racist, I know but she is Welsh and she does talk a load of shit, so it's always seemed apt.

He took Lynne's hand and kissed it. My jaw dropped. I'd not seen anything like this since I'd watched the BBC's adaptation of 'Pride and Prejudice.' Fuck me, I was back in the 1800's.

But it seemed to impress Lynne, who took me aside,

"He's got very kind eyes. Make sure you hold on to this one and don't fuck it up like you always do."

Thanks Lynne.

Chapter Fifty-Two

The one that got away; Part Three (May/June 2015)

After three wonderful days spent together, it was our final night and you could tell we were both very sad that Liam would be heading back up North the next morning.

Being a theatre lover himself, we decided to treat ourselves to a show in the West End. Felicity Kendall was starring in a revival of Noel Coward's 'Hayfever'. Being a MASSIVE Coward fan, we pipped for that.

She was absolutely stunning and gave the most amazing comedic performance I had ever seen. As the show continued, Liam placed his hand on top of mine and that's where it stayed for the rest of the performance. In that moment, I think my heart could quite easily have burst.

We arrived back at the hotel, having shared no more than a kiss over the last two nights. I decided that tonight was the night. We must consummate, okay, I know we weren't married, but that was for want of a better word.

As we lay in bed together, wearing nothing more than underwear, I slyly slipped my hand down the front of his Y-fronts. I think I went boss eyed as my hand grappled with his pork sword. I could have sworn there was a vase down there. I'd never known anything so girthy. Well, not since Darren back in 2002.

He reciprocated and slid his hands down the front of my boxers. Offended that he didn't go boss eyed at the first touch of my goods, I had to remind myself that the good Lord did not bless me in that department. But at least he wasn't telling me that he could floss with it.

As I kissed his nipples, I slowly worked my way down his body with my tongue until my mouth accidentally slipped and choked on his vase.

And choked was no joke. I'd misjudged how small my gob was in comparison to his manhood. But, with only a few tears in my eyes and gag reflex in check, I managed to perform fellatio.

Our 'first time' continued and he rolled me over onto my stomach. My pork pies widened in their storks. Perhaps, he's going to lick my back, I thought to myself. He pulled my pants down and I heard a packet rip open. Taking a cheeky glance, it was a condom. My eyes might have widened but my anus certainly didn't.

I span over to see his vase wielding a rather large johnny. Gulping, I decided now was the time to reveal my position when it comes to bedroom antics.

Let me give the non-Queer readers a little education in gay sex.

Top - the man who penetrates.

Bottom - the man who receives penetration.

Versatile - the greedy bastard who does both.

I am definitely a Top. Always have been, always will be. Ever since losing my V-plates all those years ago. I think it's all psychologically linked to me being diagnosed with IBS as a teenager.

Without sounding too graphic, I'm far too paranoid to let anyone put anything up that hole for fear of shitting all over them.

"Oh dear. Are we both tops?" I said, deflated. It had been going so well up until this point.

"No. I'm versatile!" Liam beamed.

Greedy bastard. He won't be versatile with me, I thought.

So, before you, or rather he, could say 'Top me', I had him rolled over, biting the pillow and the condom securely fastened on me. And yes, okay, I did have to swap his Extra-large one for a size more befitting of myself.

We were both rather melancholic the next morning, knowing it was time to say goodbye. Melancholic, hark at me. For a minute there, I thought Shakespeare had re-incarnated and taken over my laptop.

We kissed goodbye at Victoria station, and tears welled up in both our eyes. I stayed firmly on the platform until Liam and his train were well out of sight. I inhaled a deep breath and slowly made my way back to the tube.

Yes, we had had a fantastic time and yes, I very much liked Liam but could we really make it work being over 300 miles apart?

I'm not a needy person but if I fall in love with someone, I like to see them more often than what was destined for us.

We had a few more weeks of FaceTime and everything in our garden was rosy. Until a chance meeting with a bloke called Louis.

I bumped into him at a theatre in the West End and he started chatting me up. Flattered, he asked me out for a drink.

"How about I take you for a drink?"

"No. I have a boyfriend." I'm a very faithful guy, you know.

So Louis agreed it would be nothing more than a friendly drink.

Well, you could have blown me down with a feather. Louis was also from Newcastle and was down South, working as a stage manager on a tour of some musical, the name of which escapes me.

"How odd. My boyfriend lives in Newcastle", I told him.

"What's his name? I might know him."

"Liam."

Awkward silence.

"Liam Brown? The actor?" Louis enquired.

"That's the one. Do you know him?"

"He's my ex."

My jaw dropped open and I had to prop it up with my drink. What a small world.

"How long have you been with Liam?"

"About three months."

Louis wasted no time in revealing his trump card.

"I shagged him last week. Sorry."

Not being the violent type, I simply stood up and left the bar. I felt like I'd just been punched in the guts.

I never saw Liam again after that fateful chance meeting. But I was never bitter about it. We were having a long-distance relationship after all and every man has his needs, I suppose.

I do look back on Liam with fondness. Besides his little indiscretion, I always think of Liam as the one who got away. I truly believe that if we both had lived in London, it could have worked out. But I guess we'll never know.

And I'll always remember that he had very kind eyes.

And a cock I could have put a bunch of flowers in.

Chapter Fifty-Three

The man I thought I would marry; Part One (October 2016)

I was lashed on my faux leather sofa, knocking back a much-needed glass of Savvy B. I can't remember why it was much needed. It probably wasn't. But when it comes to Savvy B, who needs a reason?

I looked down at my phone to see a notification ping up. A Grindr notification. Looking at the half-drunk bottle of New Zealand plonk, I decided whoever it was had better be prepared to travel. I was over the limit.

"Hi. Has anyone ever told you that you've got really pretty eyes?"

Flattery. Will. Get. You. Everywhere.

And thank fuck it wasn't the usual opening line of, "can u accom?"

It soon became apparent that Rick, that was his name by the way, wasn't looking for your typical Grindr one-night-stand. He was making decent conversation. It was the first time in my gay life that I could have let my Nan cast her eyes on one of my Grindr chats.

Before we said goodnight on that first evening of conversing, he asked me if I wanted to go for a date the next day. Of course, I said YES. We agreed to meet in Windsor at 12:30 for lunch. An afternoon date. How sophisticated.

I made the decision to drive. I came to the conclusion that if I had my car, it would stop me from getting too pissed. As this is a constant error I seem to have made on dates over the years. No one likes a lush.

Well... little did I know that Rick was, in fact, a lush himself. And the date would end up with me leaving my car in Windsor, resulting in a hefty parking charge when I went to retrieve my car the next day. But I won't dwell on that and ruin the romance of this tale.

We started off in Browns, having the most delicious lunch. And my word, what an absolutely charming chap Rick was. I've just read that line back. I know I've used that word before and it sounds like I'm writing an 18th century novel, but I'm not even joking, he was a thoroughly decent chap.

As for looks, he certainly wasn't the most handsome grape in the bunch. But there was just something about him that I was immediately drawn to. He certainly wasn't the usual type of guy I would go for, but for once, I decided I should opt for personality. Besides, going for looks hadn't done me any favours in the past.

We laughed. The conversation flowed. And so did the Savvy B. Well, for me anyway. He was knocking back a well-known brand White Zinfandel. How anyone drinks that godforsaken wine, I will never know. I swear it could give you diabetes.

After a very boozy lunch, we decided to walk along to a pub opposite Windsor Castle. I say walk, it was more of a stumble. And then he performed the most romantic gesture.

Before I reveal this grand gesture, I must tell you all of a very geeky hobby of mine, of which I indulged in telling Rick over lunch. I absolutely adore visiting churches and cathedrals.

And as we stumbled to the watering hole, Rick spotted an open church and grabbed my hand, insisting we go in and have a look first, knowing how fond I am of them. I could have cried at that moment. I don't think I'd ever met a man who had performed such a thoughtful act.

After our impromptu visit to one of God's houses, we continued on our quest to find our next glass of plonk. Once inside, we found a quaint corner table on their upstairs, outdoors, balcony, overlooking Windsor Castle. We moved in closer to each other, clearly apparent we found each other insatiably attractive.

I found myself holding his hand. An act I've never been fond of in public, but it just felt right with Rick. And we couldn't take our eyes off of each other's gaze. Straight into the old pork pies, we both looked, intently.

Time went nowhere but before we knew it, it was 6:30. We'd been together six hours. Realising how intoxicated we were, we decided it was sensible to get the train home. Going opposite directions, we left each other on our respective platforms and blew a kiss across the tracks.

No physical, on the lips kiss. And no talk of a quick bunk up. Unheard of for me. I knew it must be serious.

As my train pulled away from the platform, my phone bleeped. I looked at a text message. Rick.

"That was the best date. EVER."

As my friends will proclaim, I'm not one for being soppy. But my eyes actually pricked with tears. Tears of happiness.

Within three days, we were on our second date. This time we opted for a Sunday lunch at a pub in Virginia Water. A place I childishly refer to as VAGINA waters. For those of you not local, this is a beautiful lake, on the outskirts of London, that you can walk around.

After a beautiful roast beef dinner with all the trimmings, filled with laugher, sparks and endless conversation, we went for a romantic walk around the lake. Holding hands. STOP PRESS. What had Rick done to me?

I looked out at the lake, took a deep breath and stared Rick straight in the eyes.

"I think I might marry this man."

Obviously, I said that in my head. And not out loud.

Chapter Fifty-Four

The man I thought I would marry: Part Two (November 2016)

Two dates down with Rick and we still hadn't shared anything more intimate than a handhold. This was definitely some kind of record for me. It's been a rare occurrence for me to get past the first date without a bit of How's your father.

But with Rick. Nada. Not even a kiss. Some friends thought this was a bad sign. Others believed it was romantic. I started to panic. I needed to know if that spark was there when our lips locked. As Cher categorically states, "It's in his kiss."

On our third date, which was only FOUR days after our second, (YES, we were certainly having a whirlwind romance), I decided a kiss had to happen. We had so much chemistry emotionally, I needed to be certain it was there physically too.

I booked us tickets to see a one woman show in a theatre in the West End. And the one woman was none other than Amanda Muggleton. YES, Amanda Muggleton.

I'm anticipating the perplexed looks of most readers, scratching their heads. Who the fuck is Amanda Muggleton?

Well, let me tell you. She is one of my favourite actresses from the 1980's cult classic, *Prisoner: Cell Block H*.

We sat in the theatre, watching the amazing performance (I know, I'm biased) and we were holding hands. What had this boy done to me? When it comes to friends, I have no problems expressing my emotions and feelings. But, until Rick, I'd never been very tactile when it came to men. Apart from the odd bunk up.

As we left the theatre, we decided to grab a bite to eat. We found a beautiful little Thai place that served the most delicious Green Curry. The best I'd ever got my mouth around. Rick was very cultured when it came to eating out and he was very well travelled.

We walked back towards the tube, the moonlight glistening down on the pavement and I decided now was the time. I had a duty to Cher to find out if it's really in his kiss. Without warning, I pounced like a lion on its prey.

Words will NEVER do justice to THAT kiss. But if it had been a Hollywood movie, fireworks would have been exploding above our heads and topless dancers would have been doing back-flips and cartwheels down Trafalgar Square.

I had him pinned up against the wall, sheer passion erupting from my lips, like a scene out of trashy super soap *FOOT-BALLERS WIVES*.

He finally managed to escape my grip, and my lips, and looked me straight in the eye.

"Alright Tanya Turner", he managed to say, as the blood came rushing back to his gums, tongue and lips. "I feel like Conrad when Tanya fucked him on the washing machine."

That was the best compliment any man had ever given me. Besides Joan Collins, Zoe Lucker as Tanya Turner is my IDOL. And I really could have taken Rick on a full spin cycle right there and then. But I felt Trafalgar Square wasn't the appropriate place for our first fornication.

It was time for our fourth date and we were back in Windsor, where it had all begun, just two weeks prior. After a romantic dinner date under the arches, we went for a moonlit stroll along the river. Although we didn't make it as far as the Thames.

As we went to walk past a pub, three very drunken ladies stumbled out in front of us. Rick's face dropped, faster than a whore's drawers. Confused, I looked at Rick. And then at the ladies. And then back at Rick. Rick broke the silence.

"MUM! AUNTY JOY! NAN!"

I saw the horror on Rick's face. I don't think he had intended me to meet his family just yet. And not under these circumstances.

"Dis... a very handsome boy you have here Rick", I heard a woman slur as she grabbed my cheeks. I assumed it was his Nan. Unless his mum had had a hard life.

Another of the inebriated women elbowed Rick and whispered. Well, it wasn't actually a whisper, but I think they intended it to be.

"You've done well for yourself here Rick!"

I felt myself grow a bit taller and a slight blush pop up on my face. Although Rick was mortified and he quickly said his goodbyes to his drunken relations and abruptly dragged me off towards the river.

Our fifth date arrived and I made the decision to do something I hadn't done with a man since my first boyfriend way back in 2003. I invited him to meet my friends. I planned a dinner party at my house.

We had a homemade curry and he went down a storm with my pals. Chatting, playing games and laughing. I looked at Rick interacting with my friends, and I just knew I would marry this man. How wrong could I be...

That week, he was due to go to Canada for a month to visit a friend. As I said goodbye at the departure gates at Heathrow, I did my best Tanya Turner impression and kissed him passionately up against a Terminal 5 wall.

Little did I know that that was to be our last kiss.

The weeks went by and he was due back from Canada. Excited, I planned a romantic, home cooked, welcome back, meal to mark his return. I had fillet steak, potato dauphinoise and as much as I hate the stuff, copious bottles of white Zinfandel.

But he never turned up. And I never heard from him again...

"That's it", I decided. Bollocks to men. It's going to be me, myself, and I, from now on.

Chapter Fifty-Five

Leading my first gay walk (December 2016)

Having been successfully groomed by the chairman of the Gay Outdoor Club, I was finally going to lead my first walk. A whole pack of gays, under my charge. God help them.

It was a welcome distraction to forget about that bastard Rick. Still having heard no word from him, I just couldn't believe it was possible to feel that connection for a man and then for them to just vanish. Literally off the face of the planet. Well, not quite the planet. But Canada was far enough.

So, armed with my Surrey outstanding circular walks guide-book, I arranged for my flock of queer walkers to meet at Gomshall station in the Surrey Hills.

I had planned a ten mile route, but it turned into an eight mile walk on the day, for a reason which will later become clear.

On the Friday night before the walk, I received a text from the chairman.

"I've had to release more tickets as it's fully booked."

"Oh my god", I sent back my reply, "why is it so busy?"

"I reckon it's because a young pretty boy is leading the walk."

Bunch of old perverts, I thought. But if it gets the group numbers up, I don't mind using my looks for the good of the club. I've always been keen on taking one for the team.

Sunday morning arrived and I made sure I was extra punctual to meet my pack. But disaster one was about to take place; thinking we wouldn't get more than ten or so mincers, sorry, I mean walkers, I'd picked Gomshall station for the parking. But the car park wasn't big enough as we had more than twenty signed up. And only enough parking for fifteen!

"Bugger me gently", were the first words Robert heard as he got out of his car on the morning of the walk.

Now, for anyone with early onset Alzheimer's, Robert was the man on my first walk who told me my eyebrows were comparable to the Kardashians'. Ever since, we have become inseparable. I now call him my gay best friend.

Hugging me, Robert then grabbed my face tight in his hands and told me to calm down.

"But I don't think there's going to be enough parking for all the poofters!" I bellowed.

"Listen", he calmed me, "I saw plenty of off street parking up the road. The old queers will just have to park there."

Everybody parked safely and having managed to avoid a lynching, they all gathered around me. I noticed four brand new members. And one was rather easy on the eye. I made up my mind, there and then, to make it my mission to talk to him at some point.

Becoming uber professional, I gave a welcome speech.

"Good morning, everybody. For those of you who don't know me, I'm Mark. Now this is a ten mile walk with excellent views. It covers a mix of farms, woodland and heath beneath the North Downs escarpment." I shocked myself at the big words.

Clearly, I wasn't the only one taken aback at my sudden professionalism, I noticed Robert looking at me, wondering who had abducted his gay best mate.

"Fuck it! Speech over." I saw the relief in Robert's eye that I had been returned without a ransom demand.

"Let's crack on before it pisses down with rain."

Famous last words. As it did piss down with rain for most of the walk. But that didn't ruin the enjoyment. Being seasoned ramblers, my herd of homos had waterproofs and umbrellas. Except for one. Me.

But the beautiful man that had caught my eye came to my rescue. He had a spare waterproof in his bag. Who on earth carries a SPARE one, I thought to myself? But I wasn't complaining.

"You're new", I engaged him in conversation as he helped wrap me up in the raincoat.

"Yes. I'm Billy."

"Nice to meet you."

"And you."

"I'm Mark."

"I know."

"How do you know that?"

"You introduced yourself at the beginning of the walk."

BIG HAIRY BOLLOCKS. Talk about making myself look stupid. I smiled, my big pearly whites glistening in his face, praying my looks would make up for this lapse of intelligence.

Half way through the walk, I noticed an elderly gentleman, also a new member, was struggling to keep up. Grabbing Robert's arm, my panic mode had set in again.

"Have you seen that man at the back? I hope he don't die on us. Not on my watch."

Robert, taking a glance at the poor soul, shared my concern as we saw how white he had turned.

"I hope you're first aid trained."

"Well, I am. But I did it back in 2010. But it can't go out of date, can it?"

We watched this gentleman getting slower and he started clutching his chest. Well, this sent me into heart palpitations of my own. A good slap from Robert calmed me down and I made the decision to shorten the walk to eight miles. I just prayed he could make it another three without a cardiac arrest.

Trying to impress my fellow walkers, I pointed out a special breed of cow in a field.

"They're belted Galloways!" I don't know how I knew that.

Re-enter Billy.

"Do you want to know a fact about them Mark?"

"Oh yes please", I said rather enthusiastically, eager to be educated by my new infatuation.

"They're a hybrid. Of a sheep and cow."

I was so impressed. So much so, that I went through the whole group informing them of my new found fact.

Until Robert pulled me back via my shirt collar.

"Have you been taking drugs?" he asked me.

"No, I have not!" I protested.

"I think someone's been pulling your plonker. Sheep and cows do not reproduce together. I think that'd be illegal."

"The bastard!" I screamed. "That Billy's having me on."

And then I went rushing up to said prankster and grabbed him by the back of his jacket.

"Hybrids, are they?" I shouted, rather dramatically. He just laughed, amused at my gullibility. I pursed my lips in gest and carried on leading my swarm.

Completing the eight miles, we were back at Gomshall

station. Thankfully I'd gotten everyone back safely with no one falling off a hill, or being run over by a tractor or having a heart attack. Although the struggling chap looked like he needed a stiff scotch.

Indulging in the obligatory coffee and homemade cakes, I made a bee line for Billy, holding out my tray of freshly baked lemon drizzle.

"Slice of cake?" I purred.

"I'd love a slice", he said, nearly taking my hand off.

"I made it myself. It's very moist."

Watching him eat it, I witnessed his delight at my baking skills.

"Very nice", he complemented me. "But I do prefer coffee and walnut cake. If you could make that next month?"

And I was definitely not going to say NO to Billy.

"Of course," I said as I made physical contact, rubbing his arm. And then we shared a look. Which neither of us broke until Robert screamed for more lemon drizzle.

Chapter Fifty-Six

The voicemail (New Year's Day 2017)

I woke up bleary eyed. Who made me open that extra bottle of Prosecco? I rolled over and with one eye open, I saw a missed call and a voicemail from an unknown number. It was Travis. Pissed as a fart. Making no sense whatsoever. Slurred words.

"Oh hello Mark David Morgan. I think I'd like to make an appointment. The point is. Well. This is ridiculous. I'm in a cubicle. Would I like to make an appointment? Yeah, I would like to make an appointment given the opportunity. And. Errrrrr. Oh my god. I'm so drunk. I shouldn't even be talking right now. It's ridiculous. ERM. The point is. NO! I shouldn't be talking into this microphone. Erm. I'm gonna end the call. I'm just gonna embarrass myself. Like, it's stupid, isn't it? No, I'm not going to even entertain the idea."

One whole minute into the message and I still had no clue what the hell he was going on about.

"Obviously. No. No. No. I'm not gonna do it. Like, no. Why? No, I'm not gonna do it. You're a really attractive. I, I think you're really good looking. Erm, you're a very good looking guy. Very, very good looking guy."

Okay, I thought, I get the picture. But on he continued.

"And I'm embarrassing myself by elaborating any further. So, I'm gonna end the call. I think potentially, I hope we might be able to meet independently of this. Blah. Blah. Blah. Oh shit. Anyway, what a load of old shit. I'm gonna end the call. I'm sorry. Hopefully you'll see me independently of this. Hopefully you won't even listen to this. But I do think you're a very good looking man. This is bollocks. Don't listen to this. I'm gonna end the call."

And he did. But it was too late, I had already listened to it. Maybe I'm not so undateable after all.

About the Author

About Mark David Woollard

Mark has been writing since the tender age of 8, ever since his father bought him a typewriter home from a neighbour's skip. He graduated from Brunel university in 2009 with a 2:1 BA in Creative Writing where he discovered his talent for writing comedy and melodrama. When he's not writing, he can generally be found with a glass of New Zealand Savvy B in his hand. And to be honest, he can even be found with one in his hand if he is writing!! He says some of his best work has been written whilst under the influence. He is a swimming fanatic and does 70 lengths daily. And he swears blind that his enthusiasm for the sport has absolutely nothing to do with the men in tight speedos. He is also a keen Walker. He's often out in the Surrey Hills on a Sunday, partaking in a ten mile walk. Well, he says he's got to keep his bottom nice and tight because you never know whose looking! He sits on the board of trustees for The Gay Outdoor Club, an organisation that arranges outdoor activities for members of the LGBTQ+ community.

Printed in Great Britain
by Amazon

85177262R00122